Lola

The Diary of a Red Setter

Hugh Hutchings

First published 2010 by
Edward Gaskell *publishers*
The Old Sawmill
Grange Road
Bideford
EX39 4AS

isbn: 978-1-906769-22-2

Lola
The Diary of a Red Setter

Hugh Hutchings

Typeset, Printed and Bound in the UK by
Lazarus Press
Unit 7 Caddsdown Business Park
Bideford
Devon
EX39 3DX
www.lazaruspress.com

A very special and personal animal,
not so much a pet, but a member of the family.
Supremely intelligent, extremely extrovert,
but nevertheless, a gentle, loyal
and faithful companion.

Lola

The Diary of a Red Setter

Contents

Foreword

Lola's diary was put together back in 1981 and then remained hidden away in a drawer for nearly 30 years.

When my neighbour and good friend Pat Pidler launched his book, *My Life as a North Devon Farmer*, I felt it was time my manuscript saw the light of day.

I wanted to share our experiences with dog owners and to show others how a special bond grows between dog and owner.

Times have changed. Taps on the nose are out, love and affection are in, and we are now taught to 'get inside' the dog's head and understand them. Katie in the book has become Kate and our grandchildren Lily and Alfie are growing up with our 4th Setter and we have loved and cared for them all.

With that in mind I want to spare a thought for less fortunate dogs, so 50p from each book will be donated to the Dog's Trust.

I hope you enjoy reading Lola's Diary.

Prologue

Saturday March 21st 1981

The entry in my diary read *'Baby Setters - Dulverton - Viewing Day. Went off to Dulverton in pouring rain; looked at some beautiful Setter puppies and put deposit on one. ... Roll on three weeks.'*

What that rather sparse and disjointed extract from the Diary did not convey was how cold, wet and extremely unpleasant the weather was. Relentless steely rain beat down, saturating everything on that bleak Saturday on the edge of windswept Exmoor. My wife, two young daughters and myself, soaked through, frozen, should have been thoroughly miserable and dejected. However we were completely oblivious to the elements prevailing due to the sight of eleven pairs of inquisitive and captivating eyes peering through the wire netting of the kennel doors.

The eleven pairs of eyes belonged to the Sowerhill Irish Setter Pups bred by Miss Olwen Hunt with great care and devotion, only genuine dog (especially Setter) lovers could possibly understand.

Nor did the diary show how the adult Setters had appeared from their Kennels and gathered at the edge of the exercise compounds waiting impatiently to be greeted and to shower us with affection. So typical of their breed, one pulled the flanks of his mouth back to bare his teeth in a broad smile and another so shy she would only show us the whites of her eyes from within the safety of her Kennel and momentarily slip out to the compound before disappearing again.

Following on from those displays came the Mother of the pups who in her great impatience to greet us, had bounded across to cover our waterproofs, and more important, the Girls' school macs with long streaks of mud.

Most of all though, what the diary would not have shown was the heartbreak and despair, we as a family shared when our own gentle, faithful, and deeply loved Setter Lola (who, apart from her "white glasses" bore no resemblance at all to her $10^{1/2}$ years) was diagnosed to have Leukaemia and how we had witnessed with painful helplessness her unbelievable deterioration in less than three months.

From such ill fortune only good fortune could possibly follow, and this came when we were recommended to a well respected Breeder whose dogs were sought after from Devon to Scotland and France to Canada!

As we were looking at these eleven bundles of five-week-old brown fur with their little flat, wrinkled, almost Pug-like faces watching us with great interest it seemed to me, that after one of these incredible animals had allowed us to share a home with her for so long, that period of time should not go unrecorded, and if I had made entries in diaries during that time, then why not write a diary as seen through the eyes of such an intelligent and "Humanised" animal, who, with her amazing ability to take an interest in all things around her had become a member of our family in her own right.

I therefore invite you to read and enjoy Lola's *"Diary of a Red Setter."*

Chapter One

December 24th 1970

This date has a special memory for me. Although I had not been living very long in the narrow shed which I shared with numerous other types of puppies of all shapes and sizes, I could faintly remember that there was another place before.

The only comfort from being in such a long, dim and drafty shed,was that at night we could all curl up against each other to keep warm. Very little happened during the day and those times were really boring with the only excitement being the arrival of the Kennel Maid with our food.

However there was one moment of excitement to look forward to with the sound of what I later came to know as a car, stopping somewhere near the shed. This was always followed by complete pandemonium as the puppies surged forward yapping impatiently as they waited for the Kennel Maid to open the door, gather together one particular Breed and take them outside. We would anxiously wait for the group to return, desperately searching through them to see which lucky pup had been selected. The remainder of the group would chat wistfully about the lucky one being driven away to a place called "Home."

The Kennel Maid had explained to us that eventually we would all go there - a place to look forward to and one where we would be well looked after. There was no doubt we all appreciated having someone to talk to us, treat us with respect and credit us with a certain amount of intelligence!

One thing she told us which I didn't quite understand was that when we were finally chosen we would probably go as a "Christmas Present."

As you can imagine, every time a car arrived, we all gathered expectantly at the door, waiting for the Kennel Maid and to see which lucky pup was to be chosen to be taken while the disappointment for those of us left behind had to be seen to be believed.

On this particular date I had a very strong feeling that this would be my lucky day, so every time a car arrived I rushed towards the door only to return disappointed to my corner each time another "make" of dog was collected. I had seen several pups go during my stay, but today was something special with cars arriving and pups departing with great regularity, but as the day wore on and the number of pups in the Long Shed steadily decreased, I had the uneasy feeling that I would be the very last pup left.

My instincts kept telling me not to give up but by evening I felt time had eventually run out, and I was beginning to settle down for the night and prepare for this Christmas Day everyone had been talking about, when the sound of a car stopping in the yard had every pup wide awake and peering through the darkness waiting for the door to be opened.

Can you imagine the mounting excitement when, on opening the door, the Kennel Maid started to gather all the Red Setters together, and we were all duly lined up outside in front of a tall, slim man. Immediately he knelt down to greet us I realised that this was definitely my last chance, and not wanting to waste it, I bounded forward leaping as high as I could, aiming a large long lick at his nose. There was a moment's dreadful silence as the man wiped away the moisture, and I began to wonder if I had done the right thing when to my sheer delight he turned to the Kennel Maid to say: 'This has got to be the one. ... Yes, this little baby will be just perfect.'

With my heart pounding fit to burst I was gently scooped up and carried into an Office where the man was handed my Pedigree and I had a moment to reflect on being "Perfect", mind you I always thought I was. It didn't escape my notice either that a large packet of the evil food we had been given during the stay in the long shed was handed over, but I had little time to worry about that as, with a gentle pat on the head from the Kennel Maid I was carried down some steps into the yard and towards an old blue van. The inside of the van was not unlike the long shed and as I was laid down on a blanket in the back, my poor little heart continued to pound with mounting excitement.

The van started to vibrate as it made the noise to which I had become accustomed and although I had dreamt of that moment so often, I suddenly felt very frightened and insecure as it edged its way out onto the road.

Once out there we started to bump and bounce. The faster we travelled I found it almost impossible to keep my balance and as I leaned one way then the other in keeping with each bend of the road I began to feel most unwell. Looking out through the window I was aware of trees and houses floating by which did absolutely nothing for my present condition so very carefully and stealthily I eased myself between the seats and clawed my way onto the driver's lap. Considering that by now my stomach had seen better days, I was really delighted to find myself actually helped on and gently stroked into the bargain making me feel a good deal better, especially when he started to explain how pleased he was to have finally collected me, how he had waited a long two months before driving out straight from work, on Christmas Eve, to take me Home as a Christmas Present for his wife Jane.

So although my happiness increased with each bumpy mile, I was still well and truly confused as to whether or not I was a Setter or a Christmas Present.

I settled myself down, feeling fairly happy about the way things were going and curled up into a tight secure ball, but although I probably dozed a lot the drive to "Home" proved so endless that the daylight had long since vanished allowing the countryside to be covered in a heavy blanket of darkness giving me no idea at all now of which direction we were travelling or even how far we had come since leaving the Kennels. This new problem had me completely unsettled giving a strange feeling of homesickness even though I hadn't really had one for any length of time, when a strange clicking noise made me sit up and cock my head on one side as a green light flashing in front of my nose caught my attention.

In the darkness the little flashing light shone out like a torch and I felt the van slow down until we had stopped. At long last something was about to happen and my heart began to race once more until the sound of the engine picking up speed again put paid to all that.

Expecting more travelling I settled myself down on the driver's lap, but no sooner had I found a comfortable position than the clicking and flashing had me on my paws again and this time when the van stopped so did the engine.

After the continuous sound of the engine I was acutely aware of the silence. I had little time to worry about the darkness as, without hesitation I was scooped up with one arm while we made our way through a gate and quickly up to a door which opened up as if by magic as soon as we reached it.

Standing in the doorway, silhouetted against the gentle light shining out into the darkness, was a young girl about the same age as the Kennel Maid and clearly just as friendly.

'Happy Christmas sweetheart,' greeted the man, and I was immediately thrust into Jane's arms. At once I was smothered in kisses as she exclaimed; 'What a beautiful wrinkled little face, is she really a Red Setter?'

I was expecting the man to say, 'No, she's a Christmas Present', when, thankfully it was confirmed that I really was a Red Setter, and feeling happier now I knew exactly what I was, we all went inside.

I was set down on a blanket in front of a small electric fire which, after the cold of the long shed, glowed dark red as it gave out an extremely welcome warmth, but even at my tender age I instinctively knew I should not get too close to it.

After such a day as I had just experienced , I would have been forgiven if I had fallen into a deep sleep, but such was my inquisitive nature that after enjoying the luxury of the fire for a time I thought I should explore to find out exactly where I was. Looking around I was amazed at the size of the room, although in many ways I likened it to the Kennels with all those bare floor boards and walls.

Suddenly as I was stretching myself up to my full height while enjoying a good lazy yawn, I caught sight of many coloured and twinkling papers hanging from the ceiling, snapping my mouth shut when I was half way through just to lose my balance and roll over backwards. I regained my composure in a mass of thrashing legs, but no sooner was I the correct way up than I discovered there in the corner of the room., of all things, a Fir Tree!

Well now a Setter just has to investigate such things, and I wandered cautiously up to it for a sniff to make sure I wasn't dreaming. Unfortunately that was the precise moment chosen for the tree to suddenly burst into a covering of multi-coloured lights which had the effect of stopping me in my tracks. Once I had caught my breath, a thought flitted through my head that this may be OK for older dogs to find in the dark, but not in the least convenient for me.

Jane noticed my uncertainty when the lights went on and turning to the man,said;

'She's lovely Hugh, she really is!' Then, turning back to me, went on, 'Don't worry, all this is for Christmas.'

I already knew I was beautiful, but now I knew the man's name as well and how pleased I was that they talked to me even more so than the Kennel Maid. I immediately made my mind up that Hugh and Jane were going to be my Mum and Dad from now on, and if this was "Home" then it was everything it had been made out to be.

Just as I was getting used to the comfort and warmth of the fire, and thinking I was settling down for the night, my new found luxury was rudely interrupted. Another trip out in the cold weather was the very last thing I had in mind, but being set down on Mum's lap had its consolation and really I had few complaints.

However, the events of the day were clearly taking affect on me to such an extent that I cannot remember too well exactly where we went next or indeed what happened. I do remember though how pleasantly surprised I was at hearing the clicking noise shortly after being carried from the van into a very large house, having a great fuss made of me by some very friendly people and meeting a family of Spaniels.

Again I was whisked out to the van to start yet another journey but this time I really did fall asleep and not even the clicking noise woke me. Thus the very next thing I remember was another introduction and I wondered if everyone I met from now on would always be that friendly.

After meeting another, older Spaniel there, I distinctly remember thinking that it must surely be the middle of the night by the time Dad finished the very last drive of the night by going straight into a small and extremely dark house, and also remembering how surprised to find that when taken through its door I was now back at "HOME" again.

All this visiting was far too much for a tiny Setter and had completely worn me out. Therefore when I was laid on my blanket I fell into a deep and confident sleep in spite of a niggling pain which had been troubling me all evening in my tummy.

Lola

Chapter Two

Christmas Presents

Christmas Day 1970

My very first Christmas Day arrived really early. In fact it was only two hours old when that pain in my tummy finally woke me up and, finding myself in a dark, strange place I just couldn't think what to do.

I should have been quite happy really, tucked up on my blanket beside Mum's side of the bed, but I had this terribleness inside me that was going to come out whether I liked it or not and in a panic I ran all over the place leaving horrible smelly packages wherever I went, till eventually I stumbled across my blanket and, feeling a lot better (and slimmer) I curled up, but this time I fell into a rather uneasy sleep.

Uneasy, because the room was filled with this really awful nauseating smell and it wasn't long before the inevitable happened, and Mum and Dad woke up.

They certainly are not going to be very pleased about this, I thought to myself and, sure enough, I heard an angry Dad asking what the 'blasted smell' was. Worse was soon to follow as, climbing out of bed he stepped in the biggest of the piles and stumbled across the room seeming to take great care to tread in most of the others.

The light cruelly exposed the whole bedroom for the mess that it now was with all those piles about and messy footprints covering the floor with Dad literally hopping mad.

'What a mess, what a stinking, horrible mess and it's all your fault!' bellowed Dad blinking wearily and pointing an angry finger at me. I pressed flat against my blanket and, looking extremely sorry for myself, showed Mum and Dad the whites of my eyes as I felt certain I was about to be sent back to the long kennel. There followed an awful silence as Dad washed his feet and then helped scrub the floor, muttering extremely unkind comments about 'young pups' and then washed out the bedroom with some equally evil-smelling liquid they called Disinfectant. After what seemed an eternity, they were ready to go back to bed. Dad approached me and I feared the worst until he patted me on the head while Mum smiled at me and commented, 'That *was* a nice Christmas Present you gave us!'

The next time I awoke, the darkness outside was beginning to change into daylight and I watched the bedroom gradually take shape wondering if those nasty piles would be uncovered by the early morning light, or whether it was all a nightmare. No piles appeared as the room became lighter, but on the other hand it was no nightmare either as the lingering smell of disinfectant reminded me of the events of the night.

Mum and Dad began to wake up and I worried about what effect the memories of the night would have on them, although I didn't have long to wait because Mum came over and gently picked me up to plant a kiss on the side of my nose saying, 'Happy Christmas little one, I hope you're feeling better.'

The simple answer to that was I still felt pretty rough and extremely miserable, but happily Mum and Dad stayed with me all day, staying very close and keeping an eye on me, so every time I became fidgety they hurried over to scoop me up and pop me down onto the cold and very damp mud patch outside in the garden. This went on continuously, leaving me no time at all to enjoy my first Christmas Day, in fact I honestly think that at the time I wanted the day to end as quickly as possible. Luckily, by the afternoon I began to doze a little which was just as well for my first day at home was a really uncomfortable one and by the end of it I was a real sorry sight.

Late that night I was gently taken into the bedroom and laid on my blanket thinking to myself that at least I was enjoying all the fuss and even in my delicate state I made a mental note to remember this for the future.

Happily there were no more accidents during that night, and the grey light of the following morning had already filled the room by the time I came out of my deep slumber to stare up into the anxious eyes of my new owners.

As they sat down to breakfast, the talk was all about me and how it had become most urgent to visit something called a "Vet".

Straight away we set off in the van and during the short time it took to get there I did notice how deserted everywhere was with not a single car seen en route. The "Vet" certainly was close by because the clicking noise started in no time at all and with the van pulling to a halt, the door opened to reveal a courtyard and house equally deserted as the roads.

I heard Mum say, 'It is Boxing Day, but I do hope someone is in.' After a long wait the door eventually opened, Mum holding me tight and gently stroking me while Dad engaged in a lengthy conversation with the man at the door. No sooner had Dad waved an arm in my direction than the owner indicated that we should all go inside. There we were ushered into a very small room where I was set down on an extremely cold uncomfortable table, and the man introduced himself as the vet, Mr Pettett.

I took an instant dislike to the room because, apart from obviously feeling unhappy there was that awful smell of disinfectant all around. As I lay in a shivering, pathetic heap on the table, the vet looked down at me, stroked my head and whispered, 'You do look sorry for yourself little Setter, but we will soon have you back on your feet.'

He then proceeded to give me a thorough examination and, I might add, a very personal one, for after looking down my throat and gently squeezing my tummy, he proceeded to push a glass tube into my bottom. Not the sort of thing to do to a Setter but Dad explained to me about thermometers and how they told the vet if I had a temperature or not.

After announcing that I had a bad attack of Enteritis and Worms, which really sounded awful, the Vet gave us some tablets and bid us farewell. To this, Dad thanked him very much for opening up on his holiday and we set off back home. However, even on reaching the comfort of home my troubles were not yet over as Mum held me firmly while Dad pushed a couple of the tablets down my throat before retreating to the kitchen for lunch.

I wasn't going to be left on my own though, so I wandered into the Hall to lay just where I could keep a convenient eye on any activity that might involve me. However I found it was Dad who was doing all the staring, and as he approached me he described in detail the way I was laying:

'... Looking very long and pencil slim, front paws together and pushed right forward, head tucked low and squashed between them. The tops of my back legs like huge wheels as they were spread eagled ... looking like an extended wedge shape, in fact every inch a Racing Car ... a LOLA.'

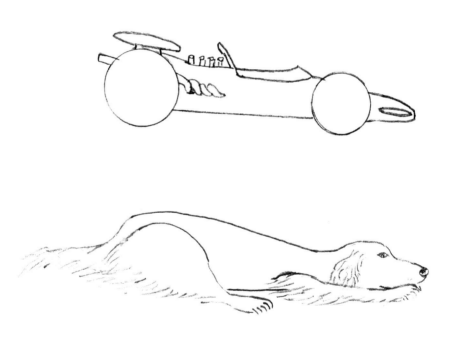

Chapter Three

The Polythene Pup

The tablets I had been given were certainly worth all the trouble taken to get them down my throat, and I began to feel a lot brighter, especially since I had left a huge and disgusting ball of worms for an unbelieving Dad to shovel up.

So now my training began, with a large piece of polythene being carefully laid down nearby every time I settled down for any length of time. I soon got the idea, no problem at all really, every time I wanted to curtsy, simply head for the polythene! Then every time a puddle appeared on it instead of the carpet I would have a fair old fuss made of me, and I could stand plenty of that I can assure you. Wherever we went, the polythene would follow, whether it was to the big house called "Wynsum", where Dad's Mum and Dad lived along with the family of spaniels, or down to Braunton where the old Spaniel lived with Mum's Mum and Dad.

I did tend to get a little confused with all these Mum's and Dad's but at least I knew which ones belonged to me!

It was at Braunton though, that the Polythene caused the greatest amusement. Every time I made my way over and curtsied, it so provided Mum's Dad with such great interest that he promptly christened me "The Polythene Pup."

Just as I had this luxury of curtsying in the warm down to a fine art, I was whisked outside at breakneck speed and dumped on the soggy mud and clay in the cold. When it was wet, that mud really was uncomfortable and I made Dad wait for hours in the freezing cold, waiting for me to pluck up the courage to lower my delicate undercarriage. Sometimes I tip-toed around for ages while the fear of touching the cold and wet ground ruined my concentration, and that was none too good in the first place.

Other times shadowy movements from across the dark garden would have me slithering stealthily through the night to find out exactly what was going on, so of course by the time my hackles had risen, and I had scared myself silly, sniffing nothing in particular, I had completely forgotten the reason I went out there.

This routine continued for a while until early one dark morning Dad woke me up and let me out for my early morning wee. I was preparing to return to my blanket when I noticed he was preparing to go out. This indeed turned out to be the case, for while the morning was still pitch black he bid farewell to Mum, and drove off alone in the van.

I remember following Mum about all day and worrying that I would never see him again, and as that long day progressed I became more and more concerned. I had obviously been spoilt since leaving the Long Shed, and now I felt my new-found security in danger, more so as by now the daylight was beginning to fade into evening. Finally, with the dark night well and truly on us and even Mum becoming fidgety, we heard the sound of the van stopping outside. Feeling *extremely* relieved I waited by the front door for my turn to welcome Dad home.

I was equally relieved to find out that I had not been forgotten either, and as I returned the welcome I learned that he had been to a place called "work" all day.

If I thought that day was bad, then I sure had a lot to learn, as far worse was to follow the following day.

Dad carried out his routine of driving off to work and I bravely resigned myself to the previous day's procedure. How mistaken I was to be!

Mum now started to act as though she was about to go out, and when I had been put on my blanket, given a large kiss on the top of my head, I watched dumfounded as she disappeared through the door to leave me completely alone.

After all the hustle and bustle in and around the house since my arrival, everywhere now seemed so very quiet by comparison and much too still.

Nevertheless I reckoned that if I was to wander about the house it wouldn't be too long before I came across Mum in one of the rooms. Not too difficult a task really, firstly because of the type of intelligent dog I was, and secondly because our house differed from the others I had visited in that it had no stairs. Therefore with growing confidence I wandered up the hall and into Mum's bedroom. It seems silly now, but I really thought that as I trotted serenely into the bedroom there would be Mum to see to my every need. But ofcourse there she wasn't. Now a strange unsettled feeling began to nag at me as I sniffed through the empty bedroom.

Momentarily, my hopes rose as I came across some clothes with friendly, comforting smells on them, and wagged my tail eagerly. Although my heart sank again, I at least had the reassurance that in this room at least was a place of sanctuary where I wouldn't be quite alone!

With this thought to help me, I wandered into the next bedroom, alongside Mum and Dad's and exactly the same size, but unfortunately only containing uninteresting odds and ends. I therefore retraced my steps to explore the very small room across the hall, but this too was most disappointing in that it contained virtually nothing and held almost no interest to me.

There was no interest at all in the tiny room in which Mum and Dad washed themselves, while the bath in which they sat after filling it with water, held a deep foreboding for me. I summoned only enough courage to poke my nose in there and once having satisfied myself of its emptiness, I set off briskly towards the kitchen.

I knew Mum spent a good deal of time there but alas, there was no luck this time. It's true I was pleased to find my water bowl, I was even more pleased to find my supper bowl containing some biscuits, and while I made a mental note of their whereabouts, they were still not the prize I was desperately seeking. My last chance then was the front room; such a large, empty, place to run around in and have plenty of fun, but on this occasion I was far from that sort of mood. It was no surprise really that the room turned out to be like all the others ...empty.

By now I was beginning to fret, even though the time I had been on my own hadn't been that long, but the point was, a baby Setter must have attention and I had long since got bored with no one to play with.

Suddenly, while climbing onto a soft chair, I caught a whiff of Mum's scent and, moving along underneath the mantlepiece I came across some objects which were just waiting to be played with.

'I'll teach Mum for leaving me on my own!' I growled to myself, almost getting frightened as I did so.

Firstly I sought out the clothes I had come across earlier and dragged some of them into the front room to keep me company. There followed a really fine time tossing the objects high in the air and chasing about after them, jumping onto the chairs and then leaping down to spring onto the wreckage scattered all over the floor. Eventually I dozed for a while, until the sound of the front door creaking open first frightened and then excited me as I rushed out to welcome Mum home.

I felt rather guilty about the damage as yet undiscovered in the front room as Mum was giving me such a nice welcome. The time I had been left on my own was only a morning, but it was a long time to a pup who needed to do so much. All these things went through my head as Mum collected together some of the clothes which hadn't quite made it into the front room, and then I slunk behind her in through the door to wait for the roof to cave in when all the wreckage was discovered.

Poor Mum sank into the chair on which I had been having so much fun earlier, and held her head in her hands.

'Lola, you wicked dog, these are our only souvenirs, how could you do such a terrible thing?'

As I watched the tears trickle down her face I felt a mixture of shame and concern at Mum being so upset, and climbed onto the arm of the chair, squeezing as close as I could, then, pushing my head against her I tried my hardest to make up for the day's tantrums.

By evening Mum was speaking to me again, but as the time approached for Dad's home-coming I began to worry what reaction would follow the report on my trail of destruction. Determined to get in first, I rushed out quickly to bestow my welcome on him in an effort to soften the blow.

I looked up with a genuine feeling of concern as the whole tale of the morning was related, and the combination of my eyes and the time since the discovery saved the day.

The next day when I was again laid on my bed, I watched the door close behind Mum and promised myself I would behave. But ... you've guessed it, within minutes I was completely bored, even after exploring all the rooms in a vain attempt to find anyone, I was bored. So there was nothing for it but to seek out some more of Mum's possessions again, and although they were a little more difficult to get at this time, it seemed to me to be all part of the game.

That's the way it continued, I just couldn't help myself and must have ruined a good many possessions while Mum cried a good many tears and the only good thing to come out of all this havoc was how much comfort and understanding I had learned to give.

Trying to get out of this habit meant more problems had to be caused in other ways, and so there was when I discovered the gap under the gate was small enough to squeeze through and have a really good look at the big outside World, until Dad put an end to that little adventure by putting wire netting there.

The only thing left, apart from common disobedience like tearing up newspapers, or scampering off with the odd shoe or two, was to chase around the back garden and toss lumps of clay up into the air.

This was indeed great fun until, one day, while chasing happily alongside the back fence, a growl from the other side caused my hackles to stand on end and double my speed instantly to reach the safety of the house. From there I peeped cautiously out, but to satisfy my Setter curiosity, I inched my way back, crouching low against the ground, as stealthily I regained my position by the fence and, plucking up all my courage, I peered through a gap.

To my sheer delight, on the other side was none other then a full grown Red Setter! How I admired his coat and splendid feathers as he stood there proudly surveying the freedom of his enormous Gardens and Orchard.

Shamus was his name, and as we chatted he told me that he was two years old, and thought a lot of the fact that he spent his nights, not in a dog basket but a car called an Aston Martin!

Even so, he was prepared to listen carefully to my childish chatter of mischief but became extremely serious when I boasted at how I could squeeze under the gate if I really wanted to.

The reason for his serious expression became apparent when Shamus explained how, one day someone had left the gate open and thinking that his luck was in, he rushed out and down the road only to be knocked over by a passing car.

Pushing out his huge, manly chest, he summoned himself to his full height and looking down straight into my eyes,grimly warned: 'Be very careful of that road Lola, never, never go on it without your owners, try and stay as far away from it as you can,' and with that he turned to walk with some difficulty back to his home.

In the sun with Mum

Chapter Four

First Walks

On my second visit to the vet, I knew exactly what to expect, with memories of the thermometer and smell of disinfectant still fresh in my mind.

It was no surprise then, as the van was parked in the courtyard, that I became filled with misgivings and energetically made my reluctance to enter quite clear.

To say there was no option would be an understatement, being whisked through the door before my paws could even touch the floor, but instead of going into the small room with the cold table, we sat down in a waiting room.

This served to take some of the tension out of the situation as, sitting on Mum's lap, I looked around to survey the selection of animals waiting their turn. Some, like me, looked nervous, others impatiently shifted about, and one or two of the older, more experienced animals, obviously wise to the situation, just relaxed, completely unconcerned by the occasion.

I'd seen a wide variety of dogs in the Long Shed, but there was one or two strange looking folk with fluffy coats, lots of whiskers and hissed if any dog approached too close, these I was informed were Cats, and I took an instant dislike to them.

Not only were the animals summing each other up, but I noticed the owners making fleeting glances at each other, wondering what sort of person could *possibly* own an animal like *that* or what could have possessed *anyone* in their right mind to have actually bought one of *those*, while others simply looked on quietly, trying to work out what ailment each of the animals was suffering from.

After a really boring wait, I was duly taken into the surgery to be stood on that cold table, and thinking back to my last visit I quickly sat down as soon as Mr Pettett produced the thermometer. All to no avail though as I was gently lifted up for my temperature to be taken.

Happily I was given a clean bill of health but my vet experience ended on a painful note as I was given the first of my injections.

Once back home in the security of the bungalow I was to be rewarded for my visits to the vet with a present.

Some present! From out of a paper bag Mum produced a narrow strip of leather and with much pomp and circumstance buckled it around my neck.

My first reaction was to scratch the wrecked thing off; this action being frowned upon severely, and I was made to walk around and actually like the thing!

I couldn't, though Mum did her best to explain that without one I would never be able to go out for a "Walk" and how much enjoyment I would miss. I tried really hard to understand, especially after the trouble I had caused, but at that time all I wanted to do was to retire to my blanket and work out how to rid myself of the leather strap around my neck.

One thing I did understand was that I was to make another visit to the vet for a second set of injections, as if the first ones weren't enough! But, when I had been given those it would *all* happen! To make it *all* happen I was to be given practice walks, and this entailed connecting my collar, which I was beginning to live with, to a much longer piece of leather called a lead, and told to trot about like a Show Dog.

I showed my disgust for the idea by sitting down firmly on the ground, blowing down my nose and flatly refusing to budge, only to be dragged along whether I liked it or not.

By the time my second injections were due, I had got myself into a fair routine, almost forgiving Mum and Dad for leaving me alone during the morning and began to accept the situation. After all, I now had a home of my own to wander around in as I pleased, and I soon began to adjust myself to sleeping during the mornings. This meant my damage to the bungalow was decreasing, plus my collar was now irritating me less and I had accepted that as well, feeling quite smart into the bargain.

So now I was ready and prepared for this "walk" everyone had been reminding me about so much.

Then at last came the big day! Mum and Dad were more excited than I was but as we made our way out into the garden I caught the mood as well when I realised we were actually going through those gates and down the road.

My excitement grew, as with each step I became more impatient to find out what was ahead and round the corner. At that precise moment deep inside me was lit the fire of desire to arrive at my destination as soon as possible - or even sooner!

Turning the corner at the bottom of the road I could see the fields splendidly green up ahead and pulled on my lead so hard that my spindly legs skidded and slid all over the gravelly surface. The fire inside me burned so fiercely now, I felt I had to get to the field long before anyone else.

All I earned for my struggles though was some whacks across the nose with a twig, but then, at long last we arrived and there was the field in all its splendour and there was me on the edge of it.

We made our way to the middle of the field and I eagerly waited for my lead to be removed so I could run and run and run.

Unfortunately, when the security of the lead was withdrawn, so was my courage as the field suddenly grew to a tremendous size, and gazing around at the endless space of grass, trees, and bushes disappearing into the distance, I longed for the security of my own front garden. Luckily Dad was quick to recognise my dilemma, understanding how the occasion had proved too much for a tiny Setter and beckoned me to walk alongside him.

This I did, feeling quite brave as long as I was second, but when he broke into a run, there was no option but to run as well for fear of being left behind. When we eventually stopped I was turned around and Mum was pointed out to me way in the distance across the field, I immediately set off in answer to her whistle.

That did it, I instantly forgot my inhibitions as I raced over to receive a big welcome before retracing my steps equally fast, feeling I could do it all day, especially with the soft grass under my paws and the air filled with wondrous and exciting smells.

'*Marvellous*' I thought, '*Really marvellous,*' but I soon began to wish my legs were twice as long, as they started to ache, and I was secretly pleased when I allowed myself to be caught while taking a rest and became reconnected to my lead.

Walking home a good deal more slowly than when I came out, with a new and most acceptable feeling of satisfaction, I made a special note of two words to add to my fast growing vocabulary. They were of course, "walk" and "field", but at this stage the task of remembering them proved most difficult especially since the next outing was to be to a place called "The Park".

To reach the park meant a short trip in the van which unsettled me initially, but turned out to be worthwhile when I discovered it to be the largest field I had ever seen.

The grass was short, smooth, and extremely well looked after, in fact the whole area seemed set aside especially for dogs, but while it proved fun to run around on, it didn't possess anything like the country smells of the field.

This obviously looked the place in which I was going to meet other dogs, and sure enough, even while I sniffed around after getting out of the van, what seemed to be the biggest dog in the world made a bee-line for me. As I flattened myself against the grass, it towered above completely shutting out the sun, and I closed my eyes to pretend I wasn't there only for the thing to start sniffing around my rear end, and after that thermometer I wasn't having any funny business like that! I whipped around, bravely snapping at its nose before quickly hiding behind Dad's legs, wishing for all the world that I could be left alone.

Once I was thankfully moved to a quieter spot, I realised it was something I was just going to have to live with, although it wasn't too bad an idea to keep a good distance between me and those rather rude dogs.

One delightful discovery I made during that morning was children. The park was full of children, and although I was kept at a discreet distance I began to feel a distinct affinity with them. Immediately I heard those tiny voices floating across the park, there started a bond between us, and I remember how I would dearly have loved to scamper off to play with them.

So now I had three important words to remember, and this became four when we set off for somewhere called the "Beach".

I really didn't think I was going to enjoy this one , involving as it did a much longer time in the van compared to the other walks. If I stayed in the back I slid about, if I stayed on Mum's lap I couldn't get comfortable, and if I was stuck down in the front I couldn't see where we were going, so it seemed ages before the familiar clicking noise announced the van was about to arrive somewhere, and I would heartily bark my approval. Unfortunately my barks would get so excited they turned into high pitched yaps, upsetting Mum and Dad more than anything else and earning me some more taps on the nose again.

By the time the van stopped, they were both nervous wrecks and I had worked myself up into such a state, that I had run around for some distance before I suddenly realised how soft and fine the ground was under my paws.

Sometimes it appeared soft, which made running very hard as my paws sunk into its golden surface while, as the ground became firmer, I could work up quite a speed. It was as it became firmer that I made my first mistake by failing to notice how wet the ground had become, and I was to be taught my first lesson on the beach.

As I ran along marvelling at the vast open spaces, a great amount of water appeared from nowhere to knock all the wind out of my body, and as I was lifted completely off my paws, deposited me back on the soft ground in a bedraggled sodden heap.

Picking myself up I angrily shook my coat, but on looking all around could find no trace at all of the offending water. This fact alone unnerved me more than anything else, and I rushed off to Mum for some reassurance.

I had no time at all to worry about my plight, because with a great crash, another of those great walls of water came splashing in to send me scampering away and stand barking bravely out of its reach as I watched the sand reappear in front of me.

The way in which everyone laughed at me gave a clue that I was in no real danger and quickly I learned the ways of the sea, and how to enjoy running on and digging up the sand, while the breeze which came in with the waves helped to dry my coat in no time.

It was most important then, that I learnt the words; "walk", "field", "park" , and "beach" as quickly as possible, for these marvellous places were to hold an unlimited amount of fun and interest to me from now on.

Chapter Five

In The Dog House

By now I was pretty clean indoors, obviously we all wanted it that way as quickly as possible, and my training was progressing, albeit rather slowly. Nevertheless I still thought I must have learnt everything.

Not so! For in addition to my training I was now to be taught some manners.

During meal times I would stare longingly at Mum and Dad as they ate, drooling heavily, to leave a slimy deposit over anything or anyone in the near vicinity.

This I was reminded on many occasions would not be tolerated, being sheer bad manners, not to be done, I had to sit there, behave, and be patient ... They must have been joking!

In the evenings, meals were taken into the front room and eaten on a low table, which was fine by me because without too much effort I could reach up and have a good sniff at what was on offer.

It was then that I developed a passion for cheese, and on finding a nice piece at the end of my nose, I just had to eat it, no matter what the punishment.

This habit came to an abrupt end one day, when the smell of cheese had me jumping up to the table as usual and easily made off with a nice piece.

Too easy, because after swallowing half of it, my throat almost burst into flames.

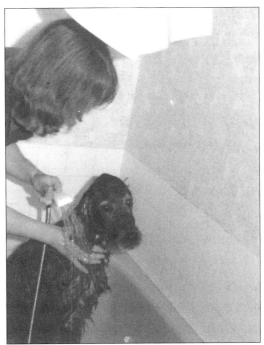

Bath time

Spitting out the remaining cheese I noticed it had been smeared with a yellow paste called mustard, and while I was gulping down a bowlfull of water to put out the terrible fire, Dad informed me in no uncertain way that I had been taught a lesson, and so I had, for I never again stole, and in return for my *good* manners, there was always a piece of cheese left for me.

Obviously a young high-spirited Setter was in line for a fair amount of trouble, this being only natural really but the day a small carpet arrived with long "fur" for the hall I really copped it!

Left on my own I was bursting to go for a wee, and in such emergencies I would make for some newspapers left by the door, but that carpet with its long hair looked so much like grass, that I did my curtsy on it.

Needless to say I was really in the dog house (*what a silly expression, nothing wrong with a Kennel as long as I wasn't in it!*)

Anyway, Mum was upset, Dad was angry, talking about how long they had taken to save up for the silly little mat, but what sent me cowering flat against the floor, was the sight of that awful white bucket filled with disinfectant which, after the Christmas happenings, was fast being associated with my accidents.

The next trouble I became involved in was complicated and started off with Dad spending ages digging in the back garden to rid it of all that soggy clay. Barrow load after barrow load was wheeled away and deposited on the dump over the field, mind you, I wasn't complaining about the extra walks and fully approved of the loads of sweet-smelling soil which was replacing all that sticky clay.

Of course, like many big tasks, and this was bigger than usual, progress was a *little* on the slow side. Slow, that is, until we came to the Easter Holiday, when the whole project made progress of devastating proportions.

Dad came home from work earlier than usual, almost catching me out, and immediately disappeared towards the Compound. I felt annoyed at being left behind, waiting patiently at the window for his return only then realising I was in the safest place, for zigzagging up the Avenue clattered the largest and strangest, not to mention the smokiest, "Wheel Barrow" I had ever seen.

The noise was easily enough to shatter my window, but how Dad could have stood it, perched on top, was beyond me and I gladly welcomed him back into the bungalow. That darn Dumper Truck was to unnerve me all evening, catching me out every time I poked my head between the curtains, and I produced a series of gentle barks whenever its hideous shape caught my eye.

Plans took a heavy blow the following day because the skies opened and drenched everywhere with a severe soaking all day. Poor Dad anxiously paced up and down, frustrated by the atrocious weather. I therefore had another evening of worry, trying to ignore the Dumper Trust, but luckily Saturday dawned hot and sunny, and more importantly, dry.

Anyone contemplating a lie in on their holiday was in for a rude awakening as Dad worked away, energetically trying to start up his new toy. His success had me, and probably the rest in the inhabitants of the Avenue rushing to witness Dad disappearing in a thick black cloud of evil-smelling smoke before jumping aboard and setting off in a series of wild swerves.

I was more than content to stay indoors during such activity and the clatter approaching from the distance was an easy early warning of his return. However, there was always a surprise to intrigue me, and as the strange machine swung into view, what seemed to be half the children on the Estate were clinging precariously to every hand hold and obviously enjoying the excitement.

Naturally the arrival of children rekindled my interest in the proceedings, and I spent a happy weekend welcoming the tiny folk or digging through the growing mountain of earth which was tumbling in through our gates and threatening to fill the garage. Some of it found a way indoors but I won't go into that, and by the end of the weekend the noisy Truck was returned to the Compound carrying the last of that annoying clay and our road returned to its usual silence.

As the new soil increased and the clay thankfully decreased, so the garden began to take shape and my troubles began.

Rushing around the garden, having a real enjoyable time, I didn't take long to scuff up my own race track, and during some extra mad sessions, could dig some fine deep holes with no trouble at all. At that moment my popularity was reduced and I was firmly dispatched from the back garden and banned from returning until further notice! I still maintained my walks though, and through a gap in the back gate watched the garden take shape, and as the weather became warmer, so the garden, as if by magic, became greener. Some steps appeared to complete the effect, and served to join not one, but two gardens, there now being two levels.

Obviously I couldn't wait to get in there amongst all the grass, chase around, up and down the banks, or try out those fascinating steps without leaving a grey trail throughout the Bungalow, but for the time being my fun was limited to the tiny front garden.

At long last the day arrived when I was finally allowed to pass the barricade and immediately set about sniffing round, padding up the steps and down the bank, but before too long my gentle inquisitive side was over-ruled by my robust, impatient side and I became more and more excited and as I did so, the nice new grass rapidly became the scruffy old grass. I began to get into gear and really enjoy myself, a deed which straight away had me relegated to the front garden.

Now came the trouble: Spending so much time cooped up in the confines of the front garden, I was always on the lookout in case anyone had been careless (or helpful) enough to leave the gate open.

This action was almost a habit. No sooner had I been let out for a wee, than I would hook my paw round the gate to see if it was unlatched. On this occasion it was, and squeezing through, I was away in a flash and gleefully set off down the avenue to explore.

Half way down, my attention was taken by a man working away in his front garden and I straight away changed direction to wriggle in and say hello.

He was most surprised to see me, although not in the least pleased because he too had been working on a garden full of young soft grass. I had obviously chosen the right moment for my visit, for I discovered the man raking stones off the surface with loving care. Barking my welcome I eagerly set about helping, quickly building up a nice pile, while my paws were tailor-made to dig up some of the more awkward ones which were proving difficult to remove.

My new found friend was obviously enjoying my company as, jumping up and down he started throwing stones for me to fetch.

Fetching stones was one thing, throwing them at me was another, but although one or two found their mark, I simply put it down to his excitement and took it all in the spirit of the game.

During this bout of activity, the grass was getting somewhat "untidy", and I thought of Dad's new garden and how angry he would have been if it was his.

During my reflections, the man cheated; creeping up on me he dived across his lawn (or what was left of it) to grab me by my scruff and drag me angrily from the garden. I had already begun to get my suspicions that all was not well, but after being led unceremoniously home the man spoke, or rather yelled at Mum in his strongest voice and my worst fears were confirmed.

Once safely inside my home I thought all my troubles would be over, but by look on Mum's face I knew very well that I was in bother once more.

Getting out of trouble was like water running off a duck's back for me, and sure enough I was soon back in the road looking for more mischief.

Almost at once I found some, but this time I was almost literally up to my neck in it!

Just across the road were a group of workmen, who, on catching sight of my wagging tail started shouting, and surprise, surprise, throwing stones at me.

'More friendly people,' I thought, and started to wriggle across the road, stopping a short way across when I recognised the angry tone in their voices. Strangely enough they didn't try to cross the road, electing to take the long route instead, but even so I couldn't escape them, even if I wanted to.

While I had waited, confused , in the middle of the road, my paws had actually begun to sink into it's unusually soft surface and being unable to turn quickly, I had become easy prey for one of the workmen, who simply lent out from the side to grab my collar.

Once again then, poor Mum received an angry knock on the door, the workman pointing to the cement on my paws while the prints left on the road told their own story. Those prints were to remain and become a permanent reminder, of my puppy days and I couldn't help noticing Dad giving them a sideways glance whenever we walked past.

There were occasions, rare I admit, when I could have fun without ruining possessions or property, or being relegated to the dog house, and one such time was when I became friends with a Siamese Kitten at Braunton.

There were in fact, two of these charcoal coloured creatures, and my normal instincts would have kept me away from them, but the darkest of the two proved most playful, and I was intrigued by its antics, even allowing myself to be lightly ridiculed by rolling onto my back and having my whiskers chewed! They were understandably, never quite the same again.

During one encounter, while laying on my back, dreaming, with the kitten chewing away happily on my whiskers, I was brought quickly to my senses by Mum's Dad.

There was nothing strange about him taking a bone-like object from his pocket and I didn't take too much notice when he put the end of it in his mouth, but when he proceeded to set fire to it I became most concerned.

As his face disappeared behind a thick smokescreen I earnestly feared for his safety, and nervously edged forward to investigate. My warning grumbles and growls were ignored completely, so I bravely placed my paws on his shoulders and eased my nose forward to protect him from the danger. Of course I burnt my nose, and hurriedly retreating amid a flurry of sneezes, I defiantly barked my disapproval from a safe distance.

Games at home though were divided into two distinct categories:

The games with Dad were quite rough, enjoyable, but I usually came off worst, while the games with Mum were completely opposite. Unfortunately what she hated most of all was my habit of nipping. I wouldn't have dared do it to Dad, but when I got excited during Mum's games, the bites got too hard, and I would end up where I usually started off ... In the dog house ! !

Chapter Six

The Journey

If my experience of travelling had been pretty uncomfortable up to now, then my next experience was to completely shatter any illusions I may have had of ever coming to grips with the problem.

One morning I awoke to a fair amount of activity, as Mum and Dad bustled in and out of the house, to and from the van, collecting items and putting them into the back of it. Something unusual was about to happen, that much I had worked out, but when I witnessed my very own blanket making its way out my worst fears were indeed well founded.

We were on the move that was for sure, but in spite of my blanket being on board, I still worried about whether I would be left on my own, although I had little time to worry about it as I was gathered up and laid on the blanket, so I worried about how long the journey would be instead!

As the van pulled out onto the main road, I had already worked myself up into a state, while the fact that we had turned away from the direction of the park had not gone un-noticed, and I therefore became more agitated as we bumped our way along, hoping desperately to be let out at the earliest opportunity. It soon became only too plain that this was not going to happen and I had memories flooding back of the long journey which I had at Christmas.

If I had thought that was long, then I was certainly in for quite a shock as this particular trip was soon to eclipse that one drastically!

I had long since given up the unequal struggle of trying to relax on my blanket, especially since it had formed the nasty habit of sliding from one side of the van to the other. My paws were no match for the slippery floor either, even with my claws out, the combination of slippery floor and bending, switchback roads defeated my uncanny skill of leaning into the corners, a skill which up to now, I had become rather proud of.

The result of this rather tiresome driving was for me to slide around the back of the van with my paws in the air! I tried everything, Mum's lap, but couldn't get comfortable on there, wasn't even allowed on Dad's lap anymore, (it was too bony anyway). I tried the floor by Mum's feet, but all to no avail, so it came as little surprise when I was well and truly sick.

I was allowed the luxury of a quick run up and down the grass verge, but then all too soon it was back to my prison in the van.

Just when I had made up my mind that we were going to spend the rest of our lives travelling, the van actually reached it's destination, which turned out to be a visit to one of Mum's Sisters, and although there was a great fuss made of me, I really was in no state to enjoy it.

Then, unbelievably after a short walk and a long boring chat, I was placed back on my blanket, to do the whole, terrible, boring and uncomfortable journey all over again.

Six hours! We were in that van for six hours! As far as I was concerned, those hours in the van well and truly finished me as far as travelling was concerned.

If I could find one good thing to say about that trip, a difficult job mark you, then it would be how that journey made all subsequent ones short by comparison.

So it was then, as we made our way to the beach, a short while after, that the trip did seem painlessly short until ... we came across an extra bumpy track.

The van crawled along this section at a snail's pace, while the sight of those mouth-watering sand-dunes approaching oh so slowly was just too much to bear.

Out came the yaps, and after the non event of the last journey, they poured out far more piercing than ever before! By the time the van had bumped its way along the final piece of track and into the Car Park, both Mum and Dad had been driven scatty.

It was beginning to look as though every trip would finish with a surprise, because as I began to calm down, there was definitely something strange about about the sand beneath my paws. Sure it was fine and soft, but mixed in with it this time was a liberal sprinkling of grass, gorse and bushes.

I was never able to master the name "Burrows" and register it in my mind, but nevertheless this marvellous and exciting place became my favourite outing. The "Burrows" were indeed interesting, a fine blend of "Field" and "Beach" with an abundance of sand sharing territory with bushes and splendid ponds. There was endless opportunity for scampering up the dunes, rolling down the other side, rushing through the long grass or chasing excitedly as I picked up a rabbit's scent, hoping for a game!

Setter Shake!

Where the grass made way for reeds, nestled the ponds, providing unlimited pleasure to run through, splashing everyone close by or simply wade about in to enjoy a good sniff, pushing my nose deep into the water, snorting, and sending plumes of bubbles cascading to the surface.

This super place covered a huge area, being extremely safe for me to wander about wherever I pleased, although I chose not to stray out of sight at any time by making large figure-of-eight movements through the dunes with Mum and Dad as the centre. After one or two collisions I learnt to skillfully avoid them at the last minute by a whisker; even while travelling at great speed.

On occasions they would disappear from view, but I could easily find them at the centre of the "eight" enjoying a rest, that is until I joined them, arriving at full speed, hot and bothered, I threw myself upon the sand for a cooling down session, and usually put paid to any relaxation!

The top sand did nothing to ease my condition, so it had to go; and vigorously digging the top sand away, I uncovered the damp and cooler layer. The warm sand had to go somewhere, and that somewhere was usually over Mum and Dad or sprinkled in whatever they happened to be eating.

As I lay there panting heavily, tongue hanging out and saliva dripping freely from it, I would often watch, fascinated, at their frantic efforts to change positions, never dreaming I could have anything to do with it!

Back home the following day I made one of my few enemies and started a permanent colour prejudice in dogs.

Finding the gate off the latch, I made my way down the avenue passing as I did, the footprints in the road and the neighbour's repaired front garden. Having successfully passed these scenes of my recent misdemeanours, and my head full of the walks I had recently taken, my dreams were violently shattered by some ferocious, high pitched yaps.

Expecting some fearsome, great beast to spring forth, I crouched low to the ground, my hackles standing erect, only to be confronted by a tiny black furry thing springing out from one of the gardens. It was making far too much noise for its size and even had the audacity to chase after me, trying its damnedest to sink in those puny teeth.

That indignity proved to be the last straw. No way was a smaller dog going to boss me about. Bigger dogs were a totally different matter, I'll freely admit that, but this noisy black effort was going to get its comeuppance, that was certain! Turning quickly, I threw myself on it, growling in my fiercest Guard Dog voice, and knocking the pathetic creature off its paws to despatch it amidst much squealing back to its lair.

The commotion had brought Dad down just in time to witness my victory, and my hatred of small black dogs was well noted and never to be forgotten.

From that day onwards, I always associated small black dogs with that noisy little poodle down the road, and I couldn't fail to notice, when we were out walking, that if we approached a black dog of any kind, then I would be tactfully removed to the opposite side of the road.

Mind you, if I had the chance, I would still have a go at the little blighter barking from behind its gate down the avenue.

Chapter Seven

Katie

July 1971

As I was growing older, I gradually became used to the habits and general running of the household, making myself quite at home, and generally feeling like part of the furniture, but just as I was getting used to Mum coming home at midday, suddenly, and not in the least unhappily she gave up work altogether. How marvellous, no more lonely mornings, although to be fair, I did sleep through most of them. I would have Mum to myself all day, not to mention all the walks to the park I was hoping to get.

I say hoped, because after one particular outing, they were seriously threatened.

The walk in question was one in which I was enjoying myself more than usual. The weather was perfect, and I was in great form, bouncing about, sniffing around, chasing children, having a real good time in fact, when suddenly something came over me, I'm not sure what, but I had a severe bout of naughtiness. When I was called to have my lead re-connected. I simply bounded off and chased about on the other side of the park. The more I was called, the more I ran about, especially when I noticed Mum had a certain amount of difficulty running after me.

Eventually, after about an hour, when I was thoroughly satisfied and tired out, I lay down to allow Mum, also tired out, to approach and fix my lead. It was only then that I noticed just how upset she had become.

During the silent walk home, I felt more and more ashamed of my actions and when poor Mum slumped into the chair for a well earned rest, I slithered up close and pressed my face against hers in a genuine attempt to make amends.

I never repeated my misconduct in the park, perhaps I felt ashamed, or more likely I had noticed Mum slowing down a good deal, sitting down more often and talking to me more than ever before. That suited me just fine, in fact it was during this time that I was taught to "Sit and Shake" on command, being congratulated and made to feel quite clever, but to be honest, once I had got the hang of it, the commands were quite easy really.

As the days got hotter, I spent many lazy days sunning myself in our new back garden, sublimely confident in the fact that I had Mum all to myself at long last. The big question was, for how long could such luxury last? This was a question I would frequently ask myself, but I was soon to get my answer, and life would never, ever be the same again.

One Saturday in mid July, I had the terrible suspicion that we were about to embark on another long journey when I witnessed a suitcase being loaded into the van. To my delight I was dropped off at Wynsum to spend an enjoyable afternoon with the Spaniels, but nevertheless I was still relieved to see Dad return and take me back up to the Bungalow.

The reason for an uneasy feeling which had been troubling me all afternoon now became apparent when I realised my family was incomplete.

No Mum! I didn't like the idea of that one little bit, and as Dad worked energetically away, painting out the small Bedroom, I alternated between laying in the Hall, and staring forlornly out of the front room picture window.

Rising from my first uneasy sleep for a very long time, I set about searching through the bungalow, all to no avail of course, and as Dad continued working away, I stretched out across the Hall in an effort to stop him leaving the Bungalow without my knowledge.

As I lay there, fairly confident that he couldn't pass without treading on me, the front door creaking open gave me an awful fright, because I wasn't expecting any movement from that direction. Drawing strongly upon my deepest courage, I convinced myself that the visitor was Mum, and eased forward to welcome her home.

Well, it was a Mum, not mine though but Dad's, who burst in excitedly to speak quickly to him. There was obviously more confusion afoot, because I was rudely bundled into the van and dropped off to play with the Spaniels again.

Before too long, Dad reappeared, alone, to take me back home but this time he could hardly contain his happiness, which went a good way towards lifting my personal gloom.

I couldn't understand at that time what he meant when he tried to explain that there would be an addition to the family quite soon. I did understand that it wasn't "quite soon" or at least, not to me anyway. Day after day I would alternate between spending my time with the Spaniels, and staring through my own picture window. During my long, patient hours by that window, I learnt the times when the postman passed by, (he seldom stopped) and when the milkman called, (I didn't trust him) but apart from these, almost non-events, very little happened to relieve my boredom.

Each evening Dad would disappear for an hour or so, and each evening I would rush out, hoping, to welcome Mum home as well, only to return indoors disappointed.

However, after many evenings, my vigilance was finally rewarded, and as the van returned, earlier than usual, the uneasy feeling that had hung over me like a black cloud, suddenly dispersed and I just knew this time would be different. Sure enough, there, silhouetted against the porch light, was the friendly figure I had been waiting to see for so long.

I hadn't been forgotten, that was easy to see, but my instincts warned me that my greeting should be toned down somewhat, and I should have the utmost respect for the tiny bundle being carried in with such care.

When my excitement had cooled a little, I was gently led over to satisfy my growing curiosity and as I eased forward, held firmly and securely, the blanket was carefully folded back.

There, nestling among some sheets, was the tiny face of a new born "Person Pup," the sight of which so delighted me, that my loving and understanding of children was firmly cemented at that one, fascinating moment.

The little "Person Pup" was to be called "Katie," and as I relaxed, thoroughly content, on the settee, I looked forward to the morning with just a little impatience, to be properly introduced.

I said life was to change now, and so it did.

I was ready and waiting the next morning, when the sounds of murmerings brought me to the doorway of the little bedroom. Venturing in I found the tiny being perched on Mum's lap, gulping down the contents of a delicious looking bottle of milk. I kept very quiet and still, fearing I would be noticed and sent packing but to my relief, a reassuring stroke from Mum meant I was allowed to stay.

I made up my mind then and there, that I would return the trust and faith put in me, and any thoughts of jealousy could be dispelled right away, for undoubtedly here was a friend for life.

After breakfast, we were to venture out into the warm mid-summer sunshine, and imagine how proud I felt walking beside the pram. On reaching the park I made sure there were no more repeats of the naughty behaviour my Setter ways had led me to perform in the past, with even the odd flash of obedience when sitting quietly beside the pram.

During my regular trips through the bungalow, I became aware of friendly, soft toys, which seemed to grow in number with every trip. The odd stuffed rabbit or kitten fooled me at first, but after a re-assuring sniff I found them delightful to play with, carrying them gently into the front room, finding a use at long last for the strange, soft part of my mouth.

Eyebrows were raised initially, but when no trace of damage could be found, I was left to carry on as I pleased !

I soon became accustomed to Katie's day, starting as it did in the middle of the night with Mum and Dad taking turns to get up for the feed. What a sight they looked too, nearly falling asleep on the chair, as they gently patted Katie on her back until she burped.

I followed with interest her movements through the day, enjoyed accompanying her on the outings, and generally learned her sounds, and what to expect. There were times though, when she would become sick, and out would come the dreaded white bucket filled with the awful disinfectant. This had me stalking off to my bed, ears and tail down, trying desperately to recall if I had made a mess or not.

I was well occupied then, looking after and keeping company with my new charge, and trying so very hard to maintain my very best behaviour, but unfortunately my image took a blow when my new Halo slipped on one particular occasion.

The temptation of the open front gate was still too much for me to overcome, and forgetting my new responsibility I was through in a flash and down the avenue. Even in my haste I remembered to keep out of trouble, and crossed the road when I neared the noisy Poodle, but in doing so, my route took me away from the field and towards a formidable new danger!

Finding myself on different territory, I began to worry, then finding myself on the main road, the worry turned rapidly to panic.

Feeling the wind from the passing cars, and my ears filled to bursting with the deafening traffic noise, all the warnings Shamus had given me, came flooding back. My blind panic drove me on and on, almost keeping pace with the danger I was trying to escape from, until with lungs almost bursting, I eventually reached a place

With Katie

where the roads parted. Here the traffic seemed to be passing in all directions, and I simply gave up, standing forlornly in the middle of them all, and praying for a miracle!

The miracle arrived in the shape of Shamus's Dad, and the whole drama came to an abrupt climax as I was dragged onto the pavement, and a safe gap wedged between one very agitated Setter and the rudest mannered drivers ever seen! The excitement was still not quite finished, because even as I lay there, being calmed down, my heart still beating at twice the normal rate, my ears registered a familiar voice calling my name.

Approaching rapidly from the hazy distance, was a tiny vehicle, zig-zagging wildly down the road, alongside the evil traffic, just as fast as its tiny wheels would carry it.

It was the cavalry arriving in the friendly, welcome, figure of an exhausted and frantic Mum, running for my very life, and I certainly would not have put any bets on which one of us was the more pleased to see the other !

The sight of Mum arriving at full tilt, together with a delighted Katie, grinning from ear to ear and enjoying every last moment, was to stay in my memory forever, while my awful experience amongst all that angry traffic, coupled with Shamus' poignant advice, virtually ensured that I never, ever, strayed onto that terrible road again.

Chapter Eight

Accidents!

After my main road incident I was repeatedly taken over the field by Dad, who made a big thing of showing me which way to turn at the bottom of the avenue, presumably in case I escaped again, and these trips served to firmly instill into my head (quite an accomplishment) to veer off towards the field and away from danger. However, they were not without enjoyment, indeed, the more we went, the more I grew to love those walks and country smells.

We would usually visit one field in particular, which meant walking past the builders' compound (houses and roads were still being built) and up to a gate. To start with, I was hoisted up by my scruff, over the gate and dropped gently down on other side.

During our walks in this field, we came across a hole half way along the bottom hedge, and not too great a distance from the gate, and, probably due to my eagerness to get in amongst the smells, I was taught to use this entrance in no time at all.

Therefore, after we had passed through the compound and Dad approached the gate, I would rush off along the hedge, nimbly work my way through the hole, and be well on my way across the field to meet him, ready for some first class exercise!

The duration of my walk would alter drastically, from covering several fields and lasting an hour or so, to a quick five minute workout. As I had no way of guessing how long any particular walk would take, I set off immediately for the nearest hedge, follow it, head down, nose on ground fashion, until I had taken in the complete perimeter and so covered as much ground as possible in case it was the five minute one.

This suited Dad just fine, he only had to make his way to the centre and from there, could call me in at any given moment.

Just as I was ever ready when the word "Field" was mentioned, so I was ready whenever the time to go was called, no matter how long (or short) the walk. I had the sense to understand that a quick flip over the field was better than none at all, and would be ready to race to my hole as Dad approached the gate, being well in position for my lead to be re-connected by the time we were in sight of the houses, and more important, their gardens!

Certainly the exercise was first class, but who would have thought that such idyllic surroundings could start off my chapter of accidents, but then, charging around the field with such abandonment, something was bound to happen.

During one of our longer excursions, we had already crossed two fields and were searching for a method of crossing to a third, when I came across an access tailor-made for me. Bounding nimbly through, I had successfully reached the next field, when I came face to face with the largest brown animals I had ever seen! Taken completely by surprise, and not in the least happy about the horns sprouting from behind their ears, I turned to beat a rapid retreat.

I should have noticed the barbed wire on the way over, but in my scramble to get back, some of the rusty barbs became entangled in my coat. I visualised those sharp points digging into me and simply stood and cried as loud as I could.

Dad, who hadn't been too far away, came sliding through the gap, much smaller now he had filled it up, and set about the problem of disentangling me. I was free in a matter of seconds, while, after careful examination, no trace of injury could be found.

"You baby! You little cry baby, I thought you were badly hurt," shouted Dad, more cross than concerned. Although his anger was probably caused by the state of his mud covered clothes, anyway, how was I to know I wasn't hurt, and those brown animals *were* getting close!

I didn't let the the incident affect my outings though, but I always had a keen respect for barbed wire, and reserved the whites of my eyes for the cows whenever they were around.

I've related before how I would sit for hours, staring through our front gate, and dreaming of the fields with their luscious smells, well it was such a thought that led to my next, and more serious accident.

Obviously I continued to check the gate, and if a crafty hook of the paw proved successful (which was rare since the road incident), then I was off to the field for a couple of minutes. I'd enjoy a quick sniff, or a game in the compound with Monty, the Old English Sheepdog pup, if time permitted.

On this occasion I had been, staring at the tatty black Poodle down the road, when from out of a garden nearer ours stalked a great grizzly Alsation. A recent arrival to the avenue, he was huge, rugged, a giant of an animal and extremely fierce, but from the safety of my garden I could raise my hackles and bark loudly at him, knowing I was in the confines of my home. Safe, that was until I absent-mindedly hooked open the gate and set off for the field.

Just as I drew level with his garden, my mind completely oblivious to anything but my destination, he sprang out at me, teeth bared and a making a fearful sound. I immediately set plan A in motion, my first plan of defence .... well, to be quite truthful my *only* plan ... to flatten myself against the ground, close my eyes and pretend I wasn't there.

When that didn't work, the beast set about me and tore a large lump of my beautiful coat completely away.

My terrified high pitched squeals brought Dad charging down the avenue, yelling at the Alsation, while I picked myself up to cry myself home, sideways, to Mum. She held me down while Dad anxiously inspected the damage, before bathing me with some evil smelling T.C.P. The wound took ages to heal, but at least it served to make my excursions to the field a little more selective!

More T.C.P. was used on me when I had my first confrontation with a black and yellow insect explained to me later as a wasp. I had always made a good job of tracking down buzzing noises and killing large annoying flies by poking them deftly with my nose against wall or window and leaving them squashed and buzz-less on the ground.

That may sound just a little sadistic, but to be fair, I did give them a fighting chance. I would only close in for the fatal poke if they were actually moving, and I had plenty of patience for these annoying buzzers. I could sit for hours waiting for them to make a move and buzz into reach ready for me to keep my lightning reflexes in trim.

There were times though, and I shouldn't really tell you about this, but all I was watching and waiting for was nothing more than a blasted spot on the wall.

I also did a good job keeping down the midges in the back garden, creating much amusement by bouncing across the lawn and launching myself high into the air in tremendous acrobatic leaps at the little creatures, while the sound of my jaws snapping together with a crack added further merriment to the proceedings.

However, this particular time I had pounced onto this wasp, its confounded buzzing had driven me mad for long enough, but when a good poking wouldn't stop it I gave it some quick snaps of my teeth. Still the little devil buzzed and when it came into contact with the soft part of my inside cheek, I felt a blinding pain the like of which, I had never felt before. In a blind panic I shot up the hall and into the bedroom, to squeeze painfully under the bed. What an unhappy, pathetic sight I must have looked as I lay there in agony, my despair made complete by my mouth swelling up to an awful size. Thankfully I didn't have long to endure this ordeal on my own for too long, before Dad came across my rump and deflated tail protruding from under the bed. Having been deeply troubled by the sudden quietness which had settled over the Bungalow, he had set about looking for me.

Needless to say, out came the T.C.P. to bathe my cheek, and I distinctly remember giving out a short, sharp, growl at the smell, to show my dislike for the stuff, but at least it helped to take that awful pain away.

From that day on, the sound of a loud buzzing would send me rushing off to the bedroom, and get myself well and truly jammed under the bed, even though my backside and tail were left out in the open completely unprotected!

Another painful experience to beset me at that time was no accident, but caused me a fair amount of discomfort never the less.

Another of Mum's sisters worked with a vet at Braunton, and I was quite pleased to recognise a friendly face after going through the waiting room routine.

Unfortunately, 1 remember nothing until waking up with a very sore tummy and being told I would lose interest in having puppies. As a pup myself, I must admit that I hadn't given the matter too much thought, but I did lap up the extra attention during the following "delicate" days.

One thing I knew for certain though, from then on, I couldn't stand any dog sniffing round my tail end, the very thought of it making me fell quite disgusted, and should one be so rude, I would immediately whip round to give the nosy blighter a couple of high pitched yaps at the end of its nose before bounding off to hide behind the nearest pair of friendly legs!

Running with the cows

Chapter Nine

The Photographer

Katie was progressing really well as far as I was concerned, so it was indeed most pleasing to see her set down on the floor for me to look after.

I was fascinated by her struggles to move about but became so frustrated at her efforts to crawl that I would nudge her much-padded bottom with my nose to help. She made it eventually, and from crawling, Katie progressed to the sitting up position, It was when she reached this stage, that we set off for what was to become one of the most catastrophic episodes of my life.

We all set off for Town, but instead of being left in the car, which was often the case, I was encouraged, yes encouraged! to come along into the busy shopping centre of Barnstaple.

However, this was to be no ordinary shopping trip, as we swiftly passed through the busy centre of the Town and made for one shop in particular.

Dad went in to have words with the owner, to return shortly for him to have a good look at me, and during the conversation, I couldn't believe my ears when I actually heard the words 'extremely well behaved and well trained Setter'. What a send up, and I was often told off for being deceitful!

The poor man wasn't totally convinced but agreed to give it a try, not knowing what he was letting himself in for, but had a little indication of the trouble to follow as soon as I had entered the door.

Happy to be allowed in, I literally got off on the wrong paw. Pulling on my lead, I was getting nowhere at all, and although I was making an excellent job of polishing an already highly polished floor, I tried desperately to stand up in my usual anxiety to be first through the door.

If I thought I was anxious, then that was nothing compared to what the owner must have been experiencing and the reason became crystal clear when I gazed around the shop.

It was like Christmas! Rows of brightly coloured lights twinkled away, while brilliant white lights revealed a whole mountain of delicate objects precariously balanced. Very foolish I thought, someone could easily knock them down, especially if they were allowed to satisfy their curiosity and have a good sniff around. I had the nasty feeling that someone else was thinking the same, and immediately felt my lead tighten to pull me to a discreet distance from the goodies surrounding me, looking as if the slightest sneeze would bring the whole set-up cascading down!

It was Dad they should frown at, not me. Morning, noon and night, all he ever seemed to do was sneeze, sneeze, sneeze! I would often just sit and watch, completely non-plussed as countless explosions poured out, and I bet he was fighting hard to control them at this moment.

I was still the source of worry though, and we quickly moved through to a far less complicated room, where the reason for our visit now became quite clear. Katie was to have her photo taken.

A young photographer introduced himself as Paul, and Katie was duly lifted onto the couch in the middle of the room, but why was he still so interested in me?

If I thought the lights in the shop had been bright, then I was certainly in for a shock, for, with a succession of deep thumps, the whole studio erupted into a mass of light, the like of which I never thought possible, while the suddenness caused my hackles to quiver and the whiskers on my nose to bristle. The increasing heat was certainly very unnerving for a Setter and was fast becoming unbearable for me inside my fur coat, while the waiting for Katie's photo to be actually taken was becoming extremely boring.

Now the interest in me became apparent, for it was intended that I join Katie on the couch, (who, incidentally, was seriously contemplating dropping off to sleep in the heat).

I was feeling very agitated at being hemmed in and had long ago lost interest in the whole proceedings. I immediately leapt from the couch to land on the polished floor with such a force, that my legs spread out and skated serenely across the room, presenting Dad with a simple task in returning me to my position.

To lie still at the best of times, outside of my favourite position at home, was like asking for a miracle, and so it came as no surprise at all, when patience began to run out and tempers began to shorten. The main problem was that I could keep still while preparations were being made, but when it came to actually take the photo, I would shift position, and then, when one was actually taken, the "Pop" from the bulb together with the accompanying brilliant flash was itself enough to frighten me off the couch again!

For a few precious moments, things went well and I admired everyone for their patience in what was fast becoming a hopeless situation, but when an empty box was casually thrown onto the floor, this indicated an end to the boredom and signalled the start of a much welcome game, which I naturally accepted most gratefully.

Leaping from the couch, I completely forgot the slippery floor, sliding gracefully across the studio and into a table at the far end. I cannoned into it with such force that a pile of papers which had been minding their own business, now found they had nothing to support them. I stopped momentarily, fascinated, as they floated lazily down making the floor nothing less than lethal, and making any attempt to catch me particularly hazardous now that nobody else could keep their balance.

In the confusion I had forgotten what it was I had been chasing and picked up the first object I came across. The frantic efforts to catch me now turned to panic, for I had only chosen a full box of flash bulbs, and while we all skidded around the room, Mum took the opportunity to rescue Katie, (who, incidentally, had given up any thoughts of sleeping, and was now really enjoying the show).

While Katie shouted encouragement from a safe distance, her retreat into a corner was not a moment too soon, because a pile of empty boxes became the next victim of my fun and games, and rapidly covered her now-empty couch.

The next item in my path was one of the large and expensive looking lights on a stand, but as I gracefully brushed it with my back legs, Paul had already spotted the danger and had positioned himself to catch it. While I watched the rescue with a certain amount of relief, it allowed Dad to easily grab my collar, and with everyone agreeing that enough was enough, I was roughly bundled onto the couch with Katie, while some photos were rapidly popped off and the whole session brought to an immediate and very abrupt halt. Certainly everyone left the shop a good deal faster than when we had come in.

Obviously, the whole catastrophic episode was never repeated and I would never be invited to a photographers' again, portraits being kept strictly to Dad's Instamatic. Even so I used to hate having to wait ages for the dreaded flash to go off, with the result that pictures inevitably made me look as if I was waiting to be shot.

Happily though, when the results of the chaotic session eventually came through the photos were really very good, Mum and Dad commenting that they were so pleased with them, all the trouble had been worth while ... just this once!

Chapter Ten

Dog Training

Sometimes Mum and Dad would get the craziest of ideas, one of the more ridiculous and futile being the decision to book me in for a coarse of Dog Training lessons.

With Katie safely dropped off at Wynsum, I was dragged along to a creaky old building, up a flight of dusty stairs, and into a dingy, equally dusty room, which must have played havoc with Dad's Hay Fever!

This room was filled to capacity with dogs and owners of all shapes and sizes, rather like a gigantic veterinary waiting room. I remember thinking to myself how funny that small dogs had little owners, while the bigger variety of dog had the larger ones. This thought, along with many others, passed through my head as, with boredom already setting in, I surveyed the whole depressing scene.

The room was so large that it needed several pillars to support the roof, while outside of those, squashed together round the walls, sat the owners, and attached to the owners sat their respective Pets.

Well, most of them anyway. Some, like me, were already agitated by being brought to such an uninteresting event in the first place, and walked impatiently back and forth, until restrained by the length of our leads. A buzz of conversation crept through the room, indicating that the majority of owners had caught the mood of the animals.

This ceased abruptly with the dramatic entrance of a large, fierce, well rounded woman who strode quickly to the centre of the room to address the nervous occupants

We were requested to sit and keep quiet, poor Dad being singled out for a black mark straight away by indulging in a bout of sneezing. The woman, ignoring his complaint, repeated her demand for silence.

Can you imagine that? All those dogs to talk to, and we were supposed to just sit there in silence.

Seeing barking came naturally to me, I was off in an instant, and had worked myself to a comfortable pitch when I was quickly "corrected". That only stopped me momentarily, and was quickly back in the swing again when ... *WHACK* ... A rolled up newspaper gave me a hefty blow across the nose.

The blow now caused *me* to indulge in a flurry of sneezes but no sooner had I shaken my head and blown down my nose with indignation, than the trainer woman clumped menacingly across the floor to inform Dad in no uncertain manner, that he should have *patience*, repeating the message loudly for all to hear; 'Patience for goodness sake. Command her to stop!'

Someone on my side I thought, a friend! Perhaps I would enjoy the lessons after all, and happily barked my approval whole heartedly as she returned to the centre. So wholeheartedly in fact, that my encouraging barks drowned even her tremendous voice, and without hesitation she broke off the lesson to turn and angrily retrace her steps, where-upon she rudely snatched the rolled up newspaper from a bewildered Dad and proceeded to beat me lustily about the nose. Patience indeed! What a joke. Indeed, the jokes just kept on coming, starting right there with the sight of all those owners (including mine) standing in a neat circle, every last one of them looking extremely serious and brandishing one of those silly rolled up newspapers.

Many more hilarious events were to follow during the short time we attended those lessons and remain forever in my memory. One of the most outstanding was the week we were all taught to sit.

The trainer woman would wave her arm about energetically and bellow out the word 'SIT!' That, however, produced a big fat zero in the reaction stakes, and so the owners were instructed to command their own individual animals.

The sound of all those owners yelling at their dogs was, to say the very least, too much, and really I couldn't see how *I* should get told off for wanting to turn the whole lesson into one gigantic romp and enjoy myself.

Most dogs were confused at what they were supposed to do, or in fact who was commanding them. So bad was the confusion, that the trainer momentarily lost control of the class and, in her panic, strode smartly across the room to pick on one small and unsuspecting man, and his tiny, scruffy, yappy hound was happily standing dreaming away and taking no notice whatsoever.

The Lady towered over him, and with a tremendous flourish of her arm, the word 'Sit' vibrated from her mouth and all around the room, with the result that the nervous little man promptly did just that, while his dog carried on dreaming serenely!

On another occasion, an immaculate owner and his equally well groomed Alsation, disgraced themselves in a wonderfully hilarious fashion.

We were taking part in a walking exercise, where each owner had to teach their dog to walk to heel from one end of the hall to the other, sit, stay and and then walk to heel back again.

Needless to say, with my impatient paws combined with the slippery floor, my pathetic efforts were a complete failure, but the Alsation thought it was all a complete doddle, and although I have to admit that he was indeed proficient at the exercise, I just hated his conceit.

However, they had just completed the first walk, and were both revelling in putting on a demonstration, looking far too smug for their own good, when the Alsation suddenly stopped to take up a familiar but embarrassing position to drop some "Dog Rocks" (Dad's Phrase, not mine). The equally embarrassed and furious owner dragged the hapless animal across the floor and down the stairs, his face bright red, while the wretched dog left an awful, smelly trail nearly all the way to the downstairs exit!

Knowing that Dad disliked arrogant owners as much as I hated bully dogs, we both enjoyed a great deal of satisfaction from the episode.

Further incidents involved a dog grabbing one of those infuriating rolled up newspapers, causing much havoc weaving in and out of the assembled owners disturbing the trainee dogs' concentration somewhat, and then proceeding to rip the detestable paper to a thousand shreds all over the floor, while my own progress, slow as it was, didn't improve when Mum and I were running round in circle, each on the end of a long lead. This was one exercise I enjoyed, that is until we had the misfortune to pass either side of one of those pillars ... I'll leave you to imagine the results of that calamity.

It came as no surprise, then,with my very slow rate of progress, plus slippery paws on slippery floors together with my complete failure to concentrate, that Dad eventually came to the welcome decision to call a halt to the proceedings.

'Enough was enough,' were Dad's comments afterwards. What an understatement!   But nevertheless, comments which were undoubtedly echoed by the more serious and conscientious owners in the class, who probably made a rapid improvement in their progress with our withdrawal.

There was no doubt whatsoever that the feeling was shared by the Trainer woman now that her chances of success had been improved dramatically by my overdue exit from her class, and I began to understand now why I was the only Irish Setter in the building!

Always in the photo!

Chapter Eleven

Night Shift

Anyone who has had any experience of Red Setters will surely accept that we are very much creatures of habit, mainly because we dread the added hassle of changing or adding to our daily routine.

I had become accustomed to, and I might add, gleefully accepted, Mum's work finishing. I had been only too delighted to learn Katie's day, I had even accustomed myself to Dad's Holidays, that confused me initially and took a little time, but I managed it eventually.

However, a change was to take place that was so weird, I could never accept it as a normal day no matter how hard I tried.

Dad's work was away in the next town of Bideford, at an Engineering firm, which alone meant absolutely nothing to me, but it's what I heard from time to time. What it meant, which really annoyed me into the bargain, was him arriving home late into the evening, and regularly I would take up a position in front of the window to wait. I didn't mind this vigil at all, in fact I surprised myself with my resilience, waiting patiently until I recognised the sound of our van, before darting into the porch to be ready and waiting as he came in from the garage.

I had timed all this to perfection, being a regular part of my day, but the shock came when the whole routine was turned on its head. Just as I thought Dad was starting a holiday, he suddenly prepared himself as if to go to work, and unbelievably drove his van away into the dusk, actually going to work round about the time I had become accustomed to him returning home.

I had a very bad feeling about it all, and stayed as close as I could to Mum, who, sensing my anxiety, gave me some explanation to help unravel this latest problem.

Dad had gone on something called a "Night Shift," and one of the reasons I was brought into the family in the first place was to provide company and protection for her through the night when it was Dad's turn to do it, "Company" I could manage, but "Protection," what could "Protection" mean?

It was pretty quiet where we lived, but in the evening nothing moved, and I mean *nothing*.

As the night wore on, I pressed closer and closer against Mum, and divided my time between watching the shadowy movements on the television, curled up in an uneasy ball and occasionally drifting into a very uneasy, shallow sleep, or tip-toeing cautiously to the curtain for a nervous glance out into the darkness should a car be so bold as to venture up to our end of the avenue to turn around.

Eventually, the time arrived to switch off the television, and without its comforting noise to take our attention, a ghostly hush descended over the bungalow. Worse was to follow when I realised I was to be let out for my late night wee. The front door creaked open just enough for me to squeeze my skinny little form through, while I made a frantic dash for the nearest patch of grass before skating back into the warm friendly light of the porch, with Mum shutting the door with a slam, and clicking down the latch almost before my tail was safely inside! We both made it into the hall at the same time, my heart now beating like a sledge hammer, and I was in such a state now, that I ventured into the bathroom, leaning hard against Mum's legs while she vigorously brushed her teeth, and the bathroom was somewhere I would normally only enter if I was dragged.

We tucked Katie up at the bottom of the bed, and I envied her innocent sleep before I learned that I wasn't going to spend the night alone on my blanket. I remembered vividly the night I was first evicted from the bedroom to sleep in the hall, the feeling of loneliness being such that I cried pitifully the whole night through.

It certainly made sense therefore, that we all slept in the same room, and as, far away as possible from that front door.

I dreaded the thought of late night callers, since I would be expected to do my "Guard Dog Bit".

With the light switched off, we settled down to some very uneasy rest, and uneasy it certainly was, not having realised before just how many noises there were in the dead of night.

Every sound was magnified with every creak from the trees in Shamus' garden, or squeaks from the fence sending shivers through my fur and my heart pounding again, breathing a sigh of relief as Mum called my name after suffering from the same problems. I was even allowed to slither carefully onto the bed for a moment, but if I kept really still, perhaps that moment would turn into all night, and with that comforting thought in mind, I made sure that I didn't move a muscle!

I maintained my stillness to good effect, and as the night wore on, no command came for me to return to the floor. Still, knowing Mum's present state was so similar to mine, I didn't really expect one.

The prospect of sleep was only slightly improved, and we had just drifted off into a very shallow sleep, when an owl hooting from a nearby tree had Mum diving under the bedclothes, and me under the eiderdown!

Suffice to say that only Katie was lucky enough to enjoy a good night's sleep and we were certainly glad to welcome the daylight the following morning. We were of course more pleased to welcome Dad, and the friendly sound of his van had me scampering joyfully to the front door.

Unfortunately all that happened then was Dad went straight to bed for the whole day, and I was continually scolded for making any sort of noise.

Can you imagine the effort needed for a young Setter to keep quiet all day? It wouldn't have surprised me in the least if I had been fitted with carpet slippers, but in any case I'm sure Mum made more noise telling me to keep quiet!

Having strained every muscle and stretched every nerve creeping round all day, Dad at last put in an appearance, but sadly, no sooner had he eaten his dinner, than he prepared for work again. Thus, as the daylight faded once again, and we watched the van disappear into the quickening darkness, we prepared ourselves for yet another creepy sleepless night. I still clung to the desperate hope that no one would call after the television went off and we retired to the bedroom to be haunted by the night noises

This went on for a whole long month, and the nights were little easier to sleep through at the end of it, the net result being, one very tired family for several days to follow.

The night shift periods were few and far between I'm very glad to say, a feeling echoed wholeheartedly by the whole family, everyone being much more settled having Dad around at night.

The responsibility lifted from me was most welcome, being only too pleased to to let Dad answer the door, and leave me to bark my head off in peace.

I was more than happy to accompany him over the field at night, feeling relaxed enough to scamper off (not too far though) through the grass oblivious to the bats or odd owl or two. It was a totally different matter with Mum however, and when I ventured out with her after sunset, we would both remember those creepy nights, staying close together and keeping the exercise to a brisk, short walk, both being extremely relieved to return to the relative comfort of the bungalow.

My walks with Dad in the dark, actually paid off dividends one night, presenting him with the solution to an ongoing problem.

The problem, not unnaturally, was caused by me, and concerned a strip of front garden which he was continually failing in his efforts to turn into grass. That strip was my favourite digging area, and any grass seed which started there, ended up in the path.

The solution at first caused my downfall. I fell into a trench! It's *not* a joke. I was walking along on sweet-smelling grass one moment and laying in a trench the next !

The top of the trench was piled neatly alongside, that is, until some of the turfs found their way into our van and thence onto that elusive patch in our front garden. Purely as a precaution against other Setters tripping over them, was the rather lame excuse.

In the light of morning I trotted out for a good dig, to be confronted by an "instant lawn", the smell of which was very, very familiar not to say likable, so I did my curtsies on it instead.

Where did the turfs come from ?

Well, I'll give you the same confusing answer Dad gave our startled next door neighbour "They fell off the back of a lorry!"

Now if I hadn't been over protective to Mum during the Night Shift period, at least I was able to offer some comfort following one particular incident

We had called at Wynsum on one dark, rainy evening, and had only stepped inside for a moment, dripping wetness everywhere, when a terrific crash had Mum and Dad rushing back into the storm.

Before I had time to start worrying about the situation, they returned, helping a very wet and bewildered man dressed completely in black. So unhappy was he that even my heartiest efforts to revive him with some energetic leaps and slurps of the face, was completely ignored.

The unfortunate motorcyclist explained how, in the poor conditions, he had run into the back of our van, been catapulted over the top, and was extremely lucky not to be badly hurt.

Eventually, after the police had called, and the motorcyclist had wheeled away his much-damaged bike, we had to return our own bent van to the bungalow. The force of the accident had pushed it onto the pavement and squashed it against a lamppost.

Everyone agreed how lucky Mum and Katie were, having left the van only moments before, and especially as she was now expecting another baby. That snippet of information bypassed me at the time, but now, in hindsight I can appreciate the importance of their escape.

I could have run home faster than the van that night as it creaked and groaned pitifully along the road, but it was in the cold light of morning, that the full extent of the carnage was revealed.

The sight of the little van, now rendered completely useless by the accident was too much for poor Mum, and while Dad surveyed the damage to confirm that this was definitely the end of our friendly transport, I accompanied Mum indoors fully aware of her distress.

I was extremely concerned at anyone being upset, especially Mum, working hard in my efforts to comfort her, and hopefully I achieved a fair amount of success, as the nature and size of our new problem began to sink in. The size of the problem was certainly too large for me to comprehend, but it seemed that the value of the wreck was nowhere near enough to buy a replacement. Dad learnt to his horror at a much later date, that the value of the number plate-

(1 D R K) turned out to be twice that received for the wreck! It was certainly a cruel world for Humans.

I was only too happy to leave them to sort out those sort of problems, mind you, if I had taken the time to work out that no van meant no burrows or beach, I would have joined them in their worries and become quite depressed, in spite of the love and affection bestowed on me at the time. I did share their concern though, for a friend lost, when I thought of the old van as the vehicle that brought me away from the long shed.

To make matters worse, Dad disappeared for a couple of days, but before I could work out whether it was holiday, double night shift, or whatever, the problem resolved itself on the afternoon of the second day. A very distinctive, crisp roar indicated that a car had arrived outside the bungalow, and parked in front of my front gate. I was intrigued as usual, but, as even Mum was interested, then there had to be something significant about the white and black car making such a racket out there in the road. Surprise, Surprise! Unfolding himself from its interior was none other than the elongated form of Dad, who had no difficulty in obtaining two volunteers to look over the latest addition to the family.

With the Mini Cooper

Anything new was of great interest to me, no matter how large or how small but to say I was fascinated by the new car was an understatement. I followed Mum around the car until we came to the rear, where I came across a huge tail poking out, and being of an inquisitive nature, just had to stick my nose into it.

Of course, every human knows all about exhaust pipes getting so hot, but to me it was a tail waiting to be sniffed, and so, not only did I get quite a shock but a very burnt and sooty nose into the bargain. I happily accepted the car, being only too pleased for us to be back on the road.

The fact that the family had to borrow money to buy it never concerned me in the slightest, the car actually being bought in a City many long journeys away. Glad I wasn't invited to go to fetch it!

I did learn its name though, a "Mini Cooper" and judging from my experience of our first high speed ride, was going to be much more suited to a thoroughbred animal named after an equally thoroughbred Racing Car!

I couldn't wait until the next time I saw Shamus, to tell him all about this latest episode.

Chapter Twelve

Lyndsey

May 1973

When Mum again disappeared for a while, I resigned myself to another period of waiting while the baby I spoke of earlier was on the way. Certainly her visit started off in spectacular style.

I was woken up one night by Mum and Dad running in all directions, collecting clothes and anything that seemed in reach, followed immediately by the car being hurriedly started up. It was smartly reversed out into the darkness, we all climbed aboard, and set off towards the Town.

Relieved that we had turned away from the pitch blackness of the park, I was only slightly happier when we all climbed out of the Car at Wynsum. Everywhere was still, black, and silent, but when there was obviously going to be no reply from the door bell, I was called upon to save the day, or night if you prefer.

Being the type of nervous dog who would bark at her own shadow, let alone any sort of noise, one of Dad's favourite jokes, from which he would draw some strange satisfaction,was to whisper 'What's that?' in my ear. This would be more than enough to send me scampering to the front door, or skidding up against the window doing my best to tear the net curtain to shreds, barking so hard it even gave me a headache.

This time though the joke was most definitely on Dad, for, after whispering the magic words to me, I charged around the front Garden in ever decreasing circles, thoroughly enjoying the game, easily evading Dad's efforts to catch me, while I gave my vocals and everybody ears in the neighbourhood a fair amount of stick !

From being pitch black one moment, the street lit up like a fuse in both directions, and as our shadows grew stronger, we noticed with a fair amount of relief, that one of the lights shining out so brightly into the night, belonged to Wynsum.

Starting me barking was easy, stopping me was a totally different matter, although by the time the door was opened and I had been pushed rudely into the house on the end of Dad's foot, I had quietened down somewhat, but a little thanks would not have gone amiss.

Once inside I made sure that little Katie had been tucked up for the night, and only then did I notice that Mum and Dad had deceived me once again, and left me to spend another night with the Spaniels.

Waking up in a strange place with the Spaniels was unnerving enough, but wandering around being unable to pick up any familiar smells was totally upsetting. However I didn't have to wait long, for the very first visitor of the day was Dad himself. He spoke quickly to his own Mum, who appeared most heartened by his news, while the happiness fairly oozed out of him on the way back to the bungalow, although by the state of him, a good sleep seemed essential.

I knew what to expect next, and quietly took up my position in front of the picture window. Happily my vigil was much shorter this time, especially due to a timely and very rewarding visit.

I was taken out to a huge building on the edge of town, and while Dad left me in the car, I surveyed the scene with keen interest. All around was a vast expanse of greenery, very well kept, well proportioned with trees, and looking for all the world like another park. The greenery stretched away into the distance, merging with the hills on the horizon, the serenity of the whole parkland being interrupted by many workmen swarming over a second building in the early stages of construction. Being used to the building still taking place at home, I took little notice and turned my attention back to the parkland stretched out before me. How I longed to be out there, to be part of it all, and suddenly I became impatient for Dad's return and some welcome exercise.

I wasn't to be disappointed either, and happily made my way to the other side of the building with him, although slightly aggravated by not being released from my lead. Prancing up and down I barked my impatience to be set free, but instead of being swiftly corrected, I actually received encouragement.

Fine, if I wasn't going to be set free, at least I could have a good bark, and willingly obliged. I stopped momentarily, as all the windows opened simultaneously, and it seemed as if every occupant in the massive building was staring out at me. As the faces continued to stare down at me, Dad tried hard to explain that they belonged to the many Mums and Nurses who were staying inside. What interested me in particular, was one very familiar voice floating down, and calling my name.

So this was where Mum came! One of my biggest mysteries had now been solved, and with this information safely stowed away in my head, I barked back my recognition most wholeheartedly.

I had the uncanny habit of overstaying my welcome, and so was immediately led away to the car.

The waiting at home, although relieved of much of its mystery, still had me taking no chances, and I remained glued to Dad the whole time. I was intrigued as he struggled down the Hall with the bed setting it up in the Front room. I was totally fascinated with the tiny carry cot laid alongside, and sensing some development was imminent, I settled in front of the picture window with Katie to wait. I didn't have too long either,before a large white van drew up and while Dad hurried outside, I watched for Mum to emerge.

This she did sure enough, through the back doors, and complete with another of those delightful bundles.

This time though, I was very much at the back of the queue, because Katie took a great deal of interest in the arrival of a real, live doll, laid with much care into the carry cot by a stern-looking District Nurse. Katie was allowed a quick look, but I soon got the message from the frosty gaze being flashed in my direction, and Dad diplomatically kept me to one side. I quietly waited my turn, feeling most impatient about welcoming the new baby, but being sensible enough to allow the suspicious Nurse to be safely dispatched.

Once this had been accomplished, Mum made a great fuss of me to show I had not been forgotten, and I was allowed my first glimpse at the new arrival. I knew exactly how to behave, withdrawing my claws to produce my safest velvet paws.

There followed a real cozy time, sleeping in the front room at night, and relaxing alongside the bed and cot by day. As things returned to normal, it was back on my bed during the night, but I accepted that most gracefully, feeling doubly important now that I had two charges.

The practice I received when Katie was tiny now served me well, and I adapted easily to the new responsibility, walking carefully beside the pram, and thoroughly enjoying the walks, with Baby Lyndsey tucked away inside, and Katie perched on a seat on top.

I had great times from then on, allowing Katie to crawl all over me, while Lyndsey pulled away at my tail, or tapped my dome with her rattle, (I wasn't too keen on that!). If a Ball was thrown for me I would smartly retrieve it, gently releasing it when my young charges demanded, It was a totally different matter with the grown ups of course, for I would tease them by gripping the ball like a vice, twisting round and tapping it on my back to increase the grip, before easily sidestepping them, and prancing away, rolling a growl as I did so. I could easily retain my possession of the ball as I pleased, only losing the game after an unfair tackle from Dad dislodged it from my mouth.

As the slow process of Lyndsey learning to crawl progressed, there were times when my own parental instincts would prove essential. When I found young Lyndsey crawling toward the fire, I instantly positioned myself between her and the danger. Of course, the fire was well protected, but nevertheless I felt compelled to guide her away, in any case I could stand the heat on my side all day, even if I ended up with a singed tail on more than one occasion.

Similarly when Katie was toddling toward the picture window, I passed to and fro in front of her, before easing her away from the glass, both acts being suitably rewarded.

So what a fine summer that turned out to be, with plenty of important tasks for me to perform, and my destructive days long gone due to my most enjoyable responsibility. Indeed, why should I destroy anything? The arrival of Katie and Lyndsey had not meant being left out of proceedings at all, in fact I became more and more loved and made to feel like an equally important member of the family.

With Lyndsey

If the family planned to travel too far for my patience to bear, I would be left at home, and although the periods would sometimes seem quite lengthy, I would settle down to sleep, soaking up the praise lavished on me upon their return for keeping a clean sheet, (and carpet) and causing no damage. I still maintained a regular round of trips to the park, although Burrows and beaches were out of limits temporarily until Lyndsey grew a little bigger, but one moment in the park on a scorching hot day, stands out above others during her first summer.

Lyndsey had been crawling around, studying the flowers, daisies in particular, when Katie suddenly took off across the park at great speed, chased by a giant bumble bee. Lyndsey immediately seized her chance to explore, and while I was relieved that the Bee wasn't chasing me, I was becoming worried about the gap widening between the two girls. The problem was; which one to choose to look after? But then Mum solved that by dashing off after Katie before she reached the road. With no problem to worry about, I chose to follow the crawler, who was now moving just as fast as her knees would carry her. I knew the River Taw was on the far side of the park, and the ground Lyndsey was making gave me cause for concern. Running in front of her, I again changed her direction, the result being most satisfactory, for, by the time Mum and Katie had caught up with us, we were situated comfortably in the centre of the park.

I had plenty of room for more praise, and there was certainly an excess of it this time, but what a difference to my earlier irresponsible performance now that I was a changed character. Still it *was* my job to look after the girls wasn't it?

I continued to enjoy my games with the soft toys, increasing at twice the rate now there were two owners, and I was allowed to play just as I pleased so long as I did no damage. I had great fun then, rolling on my back, holding the delightful creatures between my paws and nuzzling them gently with my nose. There was one time of year that I loved in particular, producing as it did a new crop of toys ... Christmas!

There was something magical about Christmas, not only for the two girls, for that unique season embraced me with its mystical charm as well.

Heralded by the shortening days, I came to look forward to it almost as much as Katie and Lyndsey. Perhaps it was the anniversary of my arrival, the additions to the soft toys, or was it the sumptuous food smells swirling through the Bungalow, or a sudden increase in a particular favourite of mine, sweets and fancy biscuits?

I would become fully aware of the impending festivities with the decorations and glitter being hung gracefully across the room, taking a keen interest in the exotic reflections as they shifted and twinkled in the glow of the front room lights,

Then of course there was the Tree. That always intrigued me, but then Christmas just wouldn't be complete without one. We would set off down to the local nursery where dozens of thickly covered trees would be piled, waiting patiently to be sold. Dad sorted carefully through them until one was found exactly fitting his requirements, whereupon he struggled home to plant it in a bucket of earth from the garden. Now if I'd dug up the garden ... ! Still I had a lot to learn about these Humans and their many strange habits.

The poor tree never grew of course, but I did enjoy the many coloured lights adorning the branches, while the parcels which were to appear later round its base held a special attraction for me. The same couldn't be said for the deadly needles which dropped off with monotonous regularity, for although I soon learnt the hard way to keep my nose out, there always seemed one little blighter lurking in the piles of the carpet to remind me not to get too close. More than once I held my paw up plaintively for the offending needle to be removed.

Festivities started for real on the very day of my anniversary after the girls had been popped into bed. They would pop back again, far too often, but once safely asleep, out would come the parcels to be piled around the tree, and provide the signal for me to investigate. I then set about the treasure trove with great relish, poking and prodding each individual present, giving them all a good careful sniff, and slow deliberate examination. During my painstaking search, I would come across a very small parcel, which, from its smell alone, instinctively knew was mine, but should I be so bold as to try to make off with it towards my bed, it would be gently removed from my mouth, and returned to the collection under the tree.

The rule was simple, strict but simple - no present to be unwrapped before the appointed hour, no matter how small, and mine was no exception. What I had been searching for then, would be revealed on Christmas morning, and after I had witnessed the unveiling of the girls' parcels and studied the contents of each and every article with a great amount of interest, the time for my own presentation would duly arrive.

Amid much ceremony, the tiny parcel would be placed in my mouth, and once I had eagerly made my way to my bed, the whole family gathered round to shout encouragement as I ripped away the wrapping. Without fail, the last shed of paper revealed a Mars Bar, and while to many this morsel may have seemed very meagre, nothing to get excited over at all, it meant a great deal to me indeed, and I appreciated being included in the festivities. I did get some extra tit-bits on my birthday at the end of October, but it didn't compare with the Christmas Mars Bar.

I can clearly remember the very first present brought home for me, an extremely hard, knobbly, large blue ball. Large, that is, by my puppy standards, for I loved to wrap my mouth around it, invariably ending up with my mouth jammed open, and making strange noises until freed from my most uncomfortable predicament which, you've guessed already, gave everyone amusement. That was one of those silly habits, each time I got into a tangle I'd get laughed at, no wonder I snorted down my nose! Apart from a little dented pride, these episodes did nothing to deter my affection for the ball, which soon became my very favourite toy. Sometimes disappearing for long periods at a time, I would nevertheless give it a warm, welcome reaction when I eventually came across it.

I soon learnt the words "Fetch", or "Where's Your Ball?", and set off eagerly searching, head down, tail up, until the friendly object was found. Overjoyed, I'd toss it high into the air, leaping up on my hind legs to catch it skillfully, before setting off towards the first interested person I came across. As I pranced across the room, I threw my head back, loosening my grip on the ball and allowing it to turn deftly in my mouth, before doubling myself in half to tap it on my back and therefore regain my iron grip. The knobbles on the ball made it easy for me to hold between my paws when laying on my back, and practically impossible for Dad to wrench from my teeth during even the most exuberant games.

The blue ball was something special then, becoming by far my most prized and used plaything and I continued to hold the deepest affection for it.

During the Christmas period everyone relaxed, and I didn't take long to work out that I could get away with many things which were forbidden at other times of the year.

Sweets and Chocolates were laid out across both the high and low tables, and nobody minded when I examined them by my poking and prodding exercise, just as long as I didn't actually touch the contents. I soon discovered that if I prodded the boxes just a little too hard, then the end box would topple over, spilling its contents across the carpet, whereby I could claim them as legally mine. This was a fine loophole in the regulations and never once did I get chastised, my crafty efforts being acknowledged as worthy of the reward.

Before I had learnt and perfected this trick however, back in my food-stealing days, I had Mum and Dad well and truly baffled.

Being bored on my own I decided to investigate the objects on the front room table. Coming across a box of chocolates, the smell was just too much to resist, and easing one out of its wrapper, I devoured its contents lovingly on my blanket. So much did I enjoy the rich flavour, that I carefully repeated the process again and again until the whole box was emptied of its luscious filling and to this very day, no one could believe I actually emptied a full box of chocolates, without disturbing a single wrapper

However, amongst the celebrations, there was one part of the festivities I disapproved of, and that was the acute smell from the coloured bottles, lined up along the low table. One sniff being easily enough to take my breath away, and send me skulking off to my bed to flash the unhappy whites of my eyes at anyone in sight. Needless to say, when Dad was in a teasing mood, I would be offered an unkind sniff from a glass containing the revolting potion.

The saying, "curiosity killed the cat" can easily be adapted to dogs, as I found out to my cost, when Lyndsey opened one particular parcel.

I had been eyeing this one up for some time, studying with great interest the odd looking and unusually shaped parcel, for undoubtedly there was an animal's, nose poking out from one end. Sure enough, the nose belonged to a beautiful horse's head, complete with handsome mane, but instead of a body, had only a pole, and for feet, only a pair of wheels. Poor substitute indeed! What a crazy animal; the head sure fooled me, but that silly body didn't fool anyone.

However, as with every other toy unwrapped, I felt compelled to sniff it, just to satisfy myself that it wasn't real, and some kind of freak. I waited and watched for an opportune moment after the girls had momentarily finished playing, and then chose my moment for an introduction. This came when the strange animal was leant against a blackboard, with its neck looped over the top.

Easing forward, I stopped as close as I dared, stretching forward until my rear legs trailed out behind me, my long body all of a tremble and hackles erect, one front leg lifted in stalking fashion, and concentration oozing from every whisker. Slowly ... *very* slowly, we touched noses.

To my horror, the horse turned its huge head slowly and deliberately towards me, its huge eyes staring straight into mine, and with a frightening nod of that head, slid slowly down the blackboard to hold me in a captive embrace.

I stood frozen to the spot as the beast hooked its head over my neck, and as enough feeling returned to my legs, I made a frantic dash for the hall. The blasted thing clung on like a leach, and as I increased my pace, so did the horse, only becoming dislodged when I passed through the doorway, into the safety of the bedroom.

At least it gave the girls some added enjoyment, and if nothing else, taught me respect for their larger toys.

Running free on Exmoor

Chapter Thirteen

Visits and Visitors

Visitors to the Bungalow were rare, while by the same token we didn't make too many visits either, but nevertheless, the ones we did receive, and the trips we made, are well worthy of comment.

Visits to Wynsum, and Braunton saw important changes in the animals which lived there.

At Wynsum, my influence may have had something to do with the introduction of a male Irish Setter named Rusty, while he was later to be joined by an English Setter who answered to the name of Skipper.

Their owners had changed names as well, for , while the red dog belonged to Dad's brother, Charlie, Skipper's owners were now known by Katie and Lyndsey as Nana Polly, and Grandad Tom, altogether much more easy for me to remember.

They were obviously more my size of dog, when I was bigger, that was, but being boys, they outgrew me quickly, and as they became older, so I seemed to shrink in size, ending up the loser when the games got rough. Being a sensible dog, when it came to getting hurt, I preferred to keep my distance, electing to keep my games to the occasional romp.

Before Skipper grew too big, he came to stay with us while his new owners went on holiday. I was only too happy to oblige and to share my bed with him, so of course during that week, we got on pretty well together. I proudly showed him around my domain, but

Lola playing Nanny to Kate

Kate may fall ...

Our Four Setters ...

Lola with Lyndsey

Pin-up Pup, Kimberley

Gentle Giant, Oliver

Fleur with Lyndsey's daughter Lily

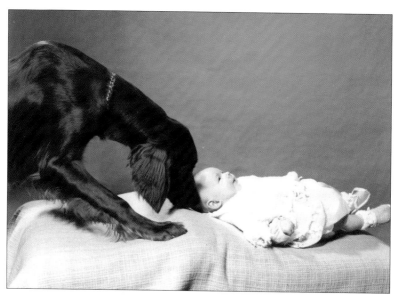

... Pull her back

That's better, Red Setter.

made sure personal toys, like my ball, were kept discreetly out of sight.

I was quite enjoying having my own visitor, but one dark evening while we were out for our late night wees in the back garden, I discovered another who gave the pair of us quite a start! We had both gone off on our own individual smelling paths, when the sound of a cough stopped me in my tracks, I froze immediately, secretly hoping the intruder was actually Skipper. Turning my head slightly, I could just make out his white form far away on his own trail beside the rose bushes, that sight alone sending prickles up my legs, through my body and into my hackles, raising them vertically as it did so. If Skipper was over there then who was over here ?

The sound of heavy breathing and the scuffing of feet would normally be enough to send me bolting, but this time I could do simply nothing, my normally nimble legs were turned to lumps of concrete, and I just stood there waiting for the monster to emerge from the darkness. I waited and waited, then, plucking up enough courage to squint through one eye I witnessed there in the blackness, a *ball*! A very prickly ball in fact, with the sweetest head and cutest pointed nose I ever did see ... so this was the monster!

I called to Skipper to come and meet the little creature, but we only had time to prick our noses once before he rolled up into an even tighter ball. My barks brought Dad out to investigate, who introduced us to Mr Hedgehog and promptly fetched some bread and milk for him.

In the morning I traced his trail, following it until I came to a small gap under the back fence. Sensing Shamus was nearby, I barked across to him and in our exchange, learnt that the little fellow lived in his orchard. Our pet Hedgehog was certainly going to be a friend for life, for I frequently came across him during the following years, while his coughs and heavy breathing certainly explained some of those spooky night noises.

With the two Wynsum Setters growing rapidly, I did well to keep my distance, as this typical example of their extrovert behaviour portrays.

When the time for exercise came around, a great old Rover car would roll up outside the gate, its rear door opened up, and all movement along the pavement in each direction, halted. The elaborate preparation was indeed justified as with a great rush, the two animals would be released from the house to launch themselves through the gate and land with a great crash in the back of the Rover. I was usually allowed the luxury of the front seat, for my safety I thought, but in reality it was for Dad's own peace of mind. Afraid that I would start the other two dogs off with my incessant barking, I was separated in a vain attempt for him to arrive at the destination with a certain amount of patience left.

Visits to Braunton were quieter with the arrival of a puppy Spaniel, but no new name to learn this time, as she was called Chum after the old lady. The owners' names had changed though, and I set about learning "Grandad George, and Nana Grace."

Being a smaller, more gentle animal, this was obviously the place to relax, and to take in a more sedate walk. I certainly didn't mind the less hectic exercise and soon learnt to moderate my own exuberance to keep fairly close to the fluffy animal.

Chum was confined to her lead for the majority of our walks in any case, but when another dog ventured too close, she would be yanked up high off the ground, to hang suspended over the offending intruder, turning gently round in the breeze with her stubby little legs dangling quietly through her harness.

I was seldom invited into other peoples' homes for fear of the damage I could cause, but I was welcomed into a Public House one day.

Mum and Dad had persevered gamely with my "anti car" condition, to take me deep into the heart of Exmoor for some excellent walks, and stopping for a rest in one of their favourite haunts; a sleepy, pretty village called Winsford. My trips to the moors were few, obviously because of my travelling problem, which was nothing less than a tragedy for me with my longing for the smells of heather and gorse, the exercise offered from the wide open spaces being unlimited. Unfortunately, Mum and Dad's patience wasn't.

This beautiful village was a treat, fitting in perfectly with the local friendly countryside, the few cars adventurous enough to venture this deep onto the moors providing little problem to the pedestrian as they wandered through its cosy centre. The freedom radiating from the little white cottages covered with straw, reached down easily to my level, making even the most mixed up pup feel wanted.

We wandered across the smallest park I had ever seen, over a tiny bridge casually made from rustic wood, and crossed a stream which went on to spill its contents across the main road. This provided both me and the girls endless fun to splash about in on such a hot Summer's day.

It was the hot weather that led me to my one and only visit to the Pub. Dad had disappeared inside to seek permission once again for the girls to enter, and returned especially pleased to announce approval for me as well. What a welcome we received inside. I wagged my tail eagerly at the fuss made of the girls, nearly winding myself in half when I too, became involved in the party.

Naturally, I was restrained somewhat from providing my "Royal" welcome in case I rocked the boat so to speak.

Along with the refreshments brought in for the family, was a sausage roll and a bowl of water, but before long, other customers were breaking off pieces of pasty and generally showering me with affection, which included topping up my water with shandy.

The girls had a good time, I had a great meal and all too soon the time came to leave, but the hospitality extended to us would never be forgotten. The only disappointment being, that as I grew to my full size, I lost the chance for a return visit.

While on the subject of the Moors and the rare visits, I must relate my confrontation with one of the round, woolly creatures known as Sheep, which itself was a rare occasion.

Much smaller than cows, which only had to lift a head to send me scampering away, they did however command a great deal more respect. For although no one minded me mixing with the cows (except me of course), no sooner was the profile of the the sheep recognised on the distant horizon, than I would be whisked away into the next field on the end of my lead, or worse still, packed back into the car. I could never understand such panic at all, dearly wishing nothing more sinister than to play around with the friendly looking "Woollys".

The time in question provided me with a good sniff, while our timely intervention most definitely saved his life.

Wandering through some high gorse on a particularly wild and deserted part of the Moor, Dad quickly ran forward, stopping to look down at something very odd indeed. On closer inspection, I satisfied myself that it was indeed a sheep and I welcomed this rare opportunity for a close up of one of these exclusive animals.

It was huge, really fat, with its great rug of wool wrapped securely, while the poor beast's legs were pointing stiffly skywards. It was still alive, but the expression on its face was ... well, nothing! The unhappy creature had just given up, allowing me to sniff it all over without batting an eyelid.

Try as he might, Dad could not budge the sheep at all, it was simply too fat and round, refusing to assist in its own rescue at all, preferring to lay there, come what may. Then Dad had another of his famous brainwaves. He had several of these of course, but to be kind, I will only stick to the successful ones.

This one was the old favourite, whispering 'What's that?' once more into my ever-receptive ear, brought me into the rescue act.

With the sheep being given one more desperate shove, my excited barks around its ears at last brought some reaction, and with legs kicking wildly, the great shaggy creature rolled over, and in one tremendous last effort, regained its correct position, to stagger away somewhat disturbed, but at least, still in one piece ! As Dad looked skyward at the black cluster of encircling birds, it seemed not a moment too soon, and I escorted the ungainly animal for a while, before responding somewhat reluctantly to Dad's whistle. Mission accomplished, we therefore retraced our steps to the parked car to relate our tail of rescue to Mum and the girls.

Visitors to the Bungalow were few, as I've said before, the big occasion of hearing the gate click, or a knock on the door, sparking off a mad rush to be first to answer, and extracting my most excited barks.

All manner of obstruction came my way in an effort to halt my progress; arms, legs, brooms, anything in fact to calm my hysterical problem, but only served to work me up all the more.

Dad now faced the dilemma of whether to allow the startled visitor inside, whereupon I would crawl across the floor, wagging myself in half and leaving a watery trail, before leaping up to convey a fairly controlled welcome, or, setting me loose outside where my watery trail would do no harm, but my uninhibited greeting toppling the startled visitor back against the gate.

It was amusing to me though, that my preference for any visitor was measured by the size of the trail, Mum and Dad obviously, being singled out for a fair old flood, everyone actually enjoying the occurrence ... so long as it happened outside.

The very first question asked of the unwary visitor therefore, was whether or not they were animal lovers.

Should the answer be 'Yes,' I was allowed to stay for a short time, never knowing when to stop my welcome (indeed, never wanting to, having an unlimited reservoir of affection inside me!)

This ceaseless greeting saw me carted off to the garage before too long, to sit in the Car, which was the place I started off should the visitor answer 'No'. I would be crammed in through the door, even before I could get in a sly lick or two.

There were times, rare I'll admit, when the odd visitor or two could actually sit around unmolested while I controlled myself perfectly. These occasions concerned small children, my natural concern for the little folk showing well, or any person I felt required my assistance.

One such important visitor came into the latter category, Grandad Tom, a truly Venerable Gentleman, and one for whom I reserved plenty time and patience. For starters he received my "Royal" welcome, reserved usually for children, after which I saw him safely to his chair, and comfortably installed.

During tea, I would take up a suitable position close to hand, laying tidily at his feet controlling myself quite admirably and keeping quiet, yes quiet!

After tea Grandad Tom would rise unsteadily to his feet, and with the aid of a walking stick, set off up the hall towards the bathroom, having me stalking beside him, gently guiding his way, but intent on keeping well away from his shuffling feet.

Once safely inside the bathroom, I would take up a characteristic posture outside, sitting down and leaning against the wall, I would lift one paw high off the floor in my concern for his well being, relaxing only when the sound of flushing water indicated his return, and standing up I then readied myself to accompany him back to the front room.

Only when I had seen him safely back to the chair could I settle down once more, receiving a reassuring pat on my dome from Mum for my concern.

These were the only times, unfortunately, when I could control myself for as I've said before, most other people received the full treatment, resulting without fail in my relegation to the garage, often on the end of Dad's foot! I could still enjoy the last laugh and gain some satisfaction from such treatment, by seeing Dad limp away - I had a very bony bum!

There were times when the traveller could spring the odd surprise on me, the most outstanding memory being the arrival of two horses, surely the most unusual animals to enter our tiny garden, and one occasion never to be repeated.

I could tell easily when someone had planned to pay us a visit, by the sudden increase in tidying inside the bungalow, our few possessions seemingly tidy in the first place. When my own personal ball itself came in for this treatment I knew visitors were imminent.

Wandering thoughtfully outside, I sat in front of my gate to sit and wait for events to unfold. That then was when I saw them. Two riders slowly approaching and heading straight for my gate. Now this was truly something to get worked up about, but even as I jumped up against the gate for a better look, it was indoors for me before I could get my second bark out.

Raising myself to my full height, I stared through the Porch window to obtain a good view of the back garden. When the horses appeared in sight, I blew down my nose indignantly; they had squeezed through the narrow gap at the side of the Bungalow, and were standing there, on *my* lawn.

What's more, they were eating it, and the roses, no wonder I barked loudly for attention. Good old Dad arrived at the double, my favourite trick had worked again, for, not wanting the neighbours disturbed, my barks would be answered day or night without fail. This time the trick worked well, and with lead attached, I was taken round for an introduction. I didn't bark this time, I felt far too nervous, but although huge, the ponies thankfully turned out to be extremely gentle, sniffing my nose and generally sharing the same interest I had in them.

One was completely white and named "Smokey", while his "oppo" was a little smaller with his white body covered in large dark patches and called "Piper".

These two fine Horses belonged to Mum's sister Sara, and her friend, and I accepted them readily, making very little noise as, watching the marks left in the lawn by their hooves, I saw fit not to cause any disturbance.

Piper and Smokey in the back garden

Taking a leaf off Dad's nose

Not only were the horses interested in *anything* growing in the garden, but their diet now seemed to take in Dad's nose, and on the face of it, not a bad idea at that! You see, in order to stop his nose peeling in the blistering heat, he stuck on a large green leaf to protect it against the sun.

We all enjoyed the heat of course, but that particular nose was an exception. However the remedy proved a failure this time, because Piper took a distinct liking for the leaf and I reckon Dad was pretty lucky to keep his nose!

After Katie and Lyndsey had been given a walk up and down the Avenue, horses and riders bid farewell, with me for one, being a little sorry to see them depart.

Finally, back to the visits, and one place that almost matched the Moors, certainly in its seclusion, was a fine wooded area known as Eggesford Forest, or as the girls named it, Egg Box Forest.

These walks took us deep into forest land, its thick, rich undergrowth filled to the brim with exciting country smells and sounds. This was undoubtedly the place to catch the sight and smells of the wild animals, most of whom weren't in the least bit wild, but rather timid instead.

These walks were most sedate, one reason being that owners of animals should be in control of us at all times, and once my frustration from the longish ride had burned itself out, this control now came easily to me.

Another reason was more simple. There just wasn't any need to hurry, for here was a place to savour, being splendidly rich in everything of interest to me, all of us in fact respecting the tranquillity and atmosphere of the whole area to spend many relaxing afternoons following the sign-posted trails threading their way quietly through majestic Pine trees.

Even paradise cannot be perfect all the time, and lurking deceptively in a valley, was a narrow bridge, gently spanning a shallow stream bubbling noisily through the undergrowth.

This rickety little bridge, charming as it may have been, presented me with a problem when my turn came to cross, but more than that, reminded me of another, much bigger bridge, which spanned the River Taw.

This terrible bridge was situated above Newbridge, only a short drive from Barnstaple, and access was gained only after a delightful stroll along the river bank, taking in the end-of-the-day summer smells, and providing more relaxation for us all. Relaxation that ended abruptly at the water's edge.

The bridge started off innocently enough, the smooth, hard path rising gently away from the river bank. Hazy country smells still in my nostrils, I trotted unsuspecting onto the bridge. Then WHAM! I completely froze, with the unnerving feeling of nothingness beneath my paws. I could only summon enough control to lower my head slowly, spying the River swirling menacingly far, far below, and I didn't know whether to move forwards or backwards. With the girls already on the far side, and shouting encouragement at the top of their voices, I had no option but to go on.

My legs turned to jelly, and, with the whites of my eyes showing vividly, I lowered myself carefully onto my tummy, and inch by inch, squirmed my way along, making painfully slow progress towards the girls.

Such was the extent of my panic combined with total abandonment, that I came in for a good deal of attention from the family, and naturally provided a fair amount of amusement into the bargain.

These little upsets however, did nothing to dampen my enthusiasm for the countryside even adding to the excitement and occasion, but even so, given the choice of crossing a river, I think I would prefer to swim across!

Chapter Fourteen

Incidents in the Park

Apart from my trips over the field, my most common source of exercise came from the Park.

A singularly delightful refuge for both Dogs and Humans alike, Rock Park spread its velvet grass along the banks of the River Taw. The river here was much, much wider, yet far less hurried than when it swirled under my infamous bridge further upstream, but having said that my Park still maintained its offer of sanctuary well away from the noisy and smelly traffic, which rushed angrily back and forth along its border.

The feeling of security, once inside the boundaries was unique, and even though the whole area split in two, with my half being the Sports Ground, there was plenty of room for all, and more than ample room available to satisfy the longest legs.

This area then, with its variety of activities, became the setting for many memorable incidents.

Even though the journey from the bungalow was comparatively short, by the time we had completed the slow, frustrating drive through the Park area, I was completely wound up, and full of bark, so it was not surprising therefore, that my arrival was nothing less than spectacular.

A suitable open space was rapidly chosen, and almost before the car had finished rolling, the door was flung open to release me like a tightly wound spring uncoiling. While the occupants of the car regained their composure, checking carefully for damage or injury, every living creature in the near vicinity would have to look to their own safety, so the car was often driven gently away to the far end of the Sports Ground to work out some of my frustration as I kept pace alongside. This not only produced the desired affect of releasing my stored up energy, and repaired some of my frayed nerve ends, but also provided me with an excellent work out at the same time.

During such exercises, I reached some impressive speeds, no doubt stepping up the training of many budding athletes, while my own road work along the more isolated stretches, could top 30 mph.

The first incident involving my presence was spooky to say the least, problems starting about halfway through an otherwise standard outing.

With no sign of a signal to bring the session to a close, I was happily padding around, completely immersed in my own little world, when the sight of a figure approaching interrupted my

A picnic at Eggesford ('Egg Box') forest

dreaming. There was nothing significant in that at first, being such a fine animal many people went out of their way to admire me. However, this visitor, now recognisable as a lady, started calling me by a very strange name, but, always happy to soak up attention, and being of friendly nature, I wandered over to investigate my latest admirer.

Imagine my surprise, after actually chastising me, she slipped a lead onto my collar and started to walk me away!

Now admiration has its limits, and this was truly ridiculous, so it was little wonder that I was confused, trying to work out what would happen next, and worrying about where I was going to finish up. Luckily for me, Dad made the next move, and hurried across for a determined rescue act before I disappeared completely from sight.

The Lady was adamant that I belonged to her, and as the discussion continued, I wondered just how this strange situation would resolve itself. It was certainly an eerie feeling having my ownership argued over, and everyone, including me, had just about reached crisis point, when the decision was made to set me free and to call my name. When I had carefully reacted to Dad's whistle, returning swiftly to my name, the poor lady sadly accepted the situation to wander away and search in vain for her lost animal, although none of us saw any sign of another Setter that day.

I would have hated being lost, my experience among the cars being a painful reminder, and especially since Skipper had told me about the time he ended up in a prison cell after he had escaped!

That strange experience in the Park never arose again thank goodness, so along with my terrorising the occupants of the Sports Ground upon my arrival, I then went on to make a name for myself among the local Cricketers.

This time Mum had taken me down to the Park with the intention of collecting Dad after a game of cricket, arriving in plenty of time to give me a good run.

Although starting off a comfortable distance away from the game in progress I soon wandered over to see what was going on. What a surprise, there in the middle of the Sports Ground, stood a group of people, dressed in white, looking extremely solemn, and seemed to me to be in dire need of cheering up.

When a small red ball came rolling my way, it seemed the perfect cue to do just that. The ball was a little hard and quite heavy, admittedly, but in spite of this, I dodged easily through the centre group carrying it, probably causing them to exercise their legs more in that moment, than during the whole evening.

I zig-zagged my way back through the players, the sound of raised voices only adding to my enjoyment, when one familiar voice came floating over above all the rest. Instead of being pleased with my antics to add spice to the dull proceedings, Dad was positively embarrassed,and becoming quite angry, so I scampered off across the Park to drop the ball, now twice the weight, at Mum's feet.

I was truly disappointed when she showed even more disapproval than Dad, so I gave up the idea, to wander off and seek interests elsewhere

My next incident concerned the old Rover car and the Wynsum Setters, and this too, was unusual.

The two boys had done their stampeding bit into the car, and we had all enjoyed a fair evening's walk, to return to the car in a most satisfyingly muddy condition. Dad opened the rear doors for us to spring onto the seat, while the family scrambled into the front.

So far, so good, but now the trouble started, and while we waited patiently, Dad tried unsuccessfully to start the car, although, in our breathless condition we weren't particularly interested anyway.

Commenting that the car had looked cleaner than usual, he shot out of the door in a panic to take on that embarrassed look again as he discovered the reason for the confusion.

While we were away, another Rover car, exactly the same shape and colour, had parked behind ours, which meant that three very muddy Setters and four pairs of boots had been wiped all over *someone else's* nice clean car.

The owner had witnessed all the events from close by, but as luck would have it, possessed a keen sense of humour, thinking the whole affair quite hilarious. Just the same, Dad wasn't taking any chances and we drove off straight away, before the joke wore off when the owner inspected the interior of his once immaculate car.

Since the Cricket incident, great care was taken not to set me free when a game was in progress, but with the square empty of players, that was the area I made for after springing from the car, and several of my incidents therefore took place on that well groomed portion.

The next embarrassing situation was caused solely by me, and although this one was a one off, like many of the others, given the same situation, I would probably do exactly the same thing again.

My inquisitive and "helpful" nature was to blame of course, and the inquisitive side came into play when I saw two figures laying on the Cricket square.

Intent on satisfying my curiosity, I moved in closer and discovered a girl being smothered in kisses, whereupon my "helpful" side took over and lowering myself onto my tummy, I squirmed forward.

What concerned me, was how quiet and still she was, and I genuinely became concerned for her safety, moving forward with such stealth that her boyfriend only saw me at the last moment, and could only stare in disbelief and silent amazement as he witnessed my efforts to revive her.

I got in some well placed and super sloppy licks before my efforts brought some welcome reaction, her eyes growing larger and larger until they almost popped out as she tried to work out what was happening. Again I was lucky that these two people shared the joke, both of them making a great fuss of me before I set off across the Park to where Mum and Dad had been keeping a discreet distance from the proceedings.

The Cricket square continued to draw my attention, and a favourite trick of mine was to dash out from the car at great speed towards the square when it was occupied by a great number of seagulls.

The chaos and spectacle created when they took off as one great flock gave me tremendous satisfaction, while as I noisily chased the squawking, screaming mass across the Park, heaven knows what injury just one of those many hooked beaks could have caused me.

However, the joke was most definitely reversed one day, after I had just completed this trick, and was running around feeling most superior. As the squawking subsided, a faint whirring from above had me gazing up into the sky, always prepared to take an interest in something new, I watched carefully as a great yellow bird descended from the sky.

This was definitely the weirdest bird I had ever seen, and as it continued to grow rapidly in size, I was sure the darn thing would blot out the entire sky while its terrifying whirring threatened, not only to strip the trees, but tear the branches off as well.

Adding to all this din came a soulful wailing as, threading their way through the Park area and cutting off my retreat, came two cars and a large red van, each topped with a flashing blue light.

"Just let anyone complain about my barks now!" I thought, as, in a panic I tripped over my own paws to land in a crashing heap of legs and an easy bundle for Dad to carry off to a safe distance.

Well how did I know what a Helicopter was, and more important, who gave it permission to land in my Park?

One of the Park's attributes is its availability during the different seasons of the year. When the roads are packed in summer I can still look forward to a run there, and similarly, when the weather closes in during the winter, the Park provides one of my only constant exercises. So that was how I came to be involved in the rescue of a fellow canine on a dark, crisp and extremely cold evening.

It was to have been a quick stretch of the legs on the way home from shopping, and while Mum stayed in the car, I disappeared into the night with Dad and the Girls.

I was putting in my usual canter, being careful to keep Dad in sight, when from out of the darkness, emerged a large, light coloured creature, breathing out large clouds of white smoke, looking enough like a dragon to have me scampering behind Dad's legs.

The creature turned out to be nothing more than a full grown Afghan, and was obviously lost and in great distress. With nobody in the Park that we knew of, the reason for his distress was obvious, and the poor lonely animal was more than pleased to allow himself to be connected to my lead.

We made our way back to the car, with the girls becoming excited over the thought of an addition to the family.

Gone were any fears of the night as we hurried away from the Sports Ground, with Mum keeping pace in the car.

On reaching the middle, the girls looked up in amazement, as, without warning Dad bellowed "ANYBODY LOST AN AFGHAN?"

A few night birds may have mis-timed their landings, but otherwise no reaction followed, even after a second attempt, so it was back to the car for further discussion.

Due to the animal's reluctance to enter the car, the decision was made to lock the two of us safely in the Children's' Play Compound, while Mum and the Girls made their way to the Park entrance, and Dad tore off to an Afghan owner he knew.

My new charge had obviously had enough, and kept close to me for protection. Me! I ask you, at that time I was trying to hide away from my own shadow.

We didn't have long to worry much more, before the sound of approaching footsteps announced the arrival of the family accompanied by the very worried owner.

As Dad duly packed us all back into the car, we bid farewell to one extremely happy dog and equally relieved owner, to make our way home, satisfied of a good deed well done, and a timely reminder for me never to stray too far from the family fold.

We always tried hard to abide by the rules and regulations governing the Park area, and my final adventure, not only changed the regulations but I felt that the Park was never quite the same again.

One thing that Dad was adamant about, was to never allow me near the muddy banks of the river. One reason being that he once owned a spaniel pup which contracted a fatal skin decease after continually coming into contact with the muddy water. The second reason was the dreadful stench from the grey mud laying thickly on its banks

One of my more unusual habits was to roll in any interesting mess that took my fancy. This would include sheep or horse mess, really anything smelly enough to take my fancy, although this action virtually guaranteed a "crack up" for anyone exercising me at the time.

This time I had strayed onto the bank while having a good time with a passing friendly dog. Finding my paws sinking gently into the mud, I was most impressed by the smell, so gleefully rolling onto my back, I immersed myself in the delightful gunge, making sure of a complete coverage with some hearty wriggling.

Working myself deeper and deeper, I turned and rolled easily on the slippery surface until there wasn't an inch of fur that had not turned a greasy, smelly grey!

I was brought down to Earth (soft as it was) by the sound of my familiar whistle summoning me back to the Park. Realising the fearful mess I was in, I sheepishly wandered back onto the grass to give myself up.

Poor Dad couldn't believe his eyes, but the stench soon confirmed his worst fears, and once over the shock, wasn't he angry, everyone in the Park sharing my chastisement.

So awful was my state, that the number one priority was to cease yelling, and to remove the evil smelling slime before it dried and became caked in my silky fur. The situation was indeed urgent, and had to be rectified immediately before I contaminated car, house or anything else with which I came into contact.

I knew when Dad's brain was working overtime, so when my scruff was suddenly grabbed I had the uneasy feeling the remedy was going to be drastic.

Drastic it certainly was! After being dragged towards the Children's' Boating Pond across the road, I was launched without hesitation through the air to land upside down in a mixture of thrashing legs and spray! That was exactly the result planned, for not only did my struggles satisfy some of Dad's pent-up fury, but also served to dislodge much of the mud to such good effect, that by the time I had reached the edge to receive another ducking, I was becoming more of a Red Setter and less a Grey Seal.

Giving myself one of my famous "Setter Shakes" I noticed Dad's concern for the grey cloud spreading slowly across the pool. There was only one action to take, and we were well skilled indeed to take it. We beat a hasty retreat!

My troubles hadn't finished, even upon arrival at the Bungalow, in fact, they were restarting, and restarting with a vengeance, as I was forced into the bathroom to begin an unhappy association with the bath.

What an unpleasant contraption, no sooner was I dumped in, than I slipped over on its highly polished surface. The more I scratched and skidded, the more anxious I became to escape from my confinement, but with no chance to keep my balance, and legs slipping in all directions, I was certainly fighting a losing battle to escape. To add to my panic, the bath began to fill with water, and the walls were rapidly turning a muddy grey.

In a valiant effort to save the bungalow from becoming flooded, Dad stripped off to get in with me, and while he kept my struggles under a certain amount of control, Mum scrubbed me clean. But still they weren't satisfied, and my torture didn't finish there, because out came the shampoo.

It made my fur wonderfully soft admittedly, but what a poofy smell, I think I preferred the mud.

So now I had an extra word to add to my collection, the very mention of "bath" being sufficient to send me stalking off to my bed with my ears well down!

However, the final word on this incident came later, during a regular visit to the Park.

Wandering past the dreaded boating pond, we came across two workmen erecting a sign at the far end.

Stepping forward to read it, Dad gave a quiet chuckle and shortly afterwards, when we were safely out of earshot, conveyed the message to me. 'In the interests of hygiene, Dogs are not allowed in the Boating Pond.'

I was given a friendly pat before continuing the walk, but nevertheless we both took great care to keep well away from the river!

Chapter Fifteen

Bedlam on the Beach

Apart from the lack of country smells, runs on the Beach were something to look forward to, with their endless expanse of soft golden sand, open spaces and exhilarating breezes allowing the utmost enjoyment and freedom.

In spite of all this freedom, and being so well occupied, my exploits could still land me in hot water.

Several faults I have covered already, but if your memory is a patch on mine then you won't mind a little reminding.

Obviously, I would get off on the wrong paw with my hysterical barking, sparked off by the clicking of the winker lights. They were different in our white car, but made the same noise. Patience was pretty thin then, by the time I exploded from the car, and I was lucky not to be taken home straight away on more than one occasion.

The wide open spaces played a prominent part in tempering the situation, the vast, unlimited sands and dunes of Saunton being excellent for repairing frayed nerves.

That was fine as long as we kept moving, but when the family stopped, as often was the case when the girls had a picnic, then problems began.

As Mum and Dad had already found out to their cost, picnics would be coated with a liberal covering of sand, while my impatient, ear-splitting yaps branded me the most hated dog on the beach.

A fine example of this problem, was the day we visited a quaint, little Beach near Ilfracombe, called Lee Bay.

The Beach itself was tremendous, a mixture of greenery, rock pools and sand, just the place to be on a hot summer day in fact.

Unfortunately, not only had the long journey upset me, but after we had successfully made our way along a very interesting rocky path, we came upon a tiny shingle beach. For Human purposes, this was probably perfect, for an energetic dog - completely unacceptable.

For about half an hour I sniffed around, paddled in the refreshing sea, or tried to make friends with some of the occupants. The sun was so hot, that no one was in the least bit interested in me, let alone moving around very much, so inevitably, my frustration grew and grew, until the high pitched, impatient yaps spilled out.

First of all I frightened myself, for the close confines of the surrounding cliffs and rocks sent my barks bouncing from one side of the Bay to the other, until I couldn't tell which was the original and which was echo. I just had to bark louder to find out, which in turn had the immediate effect of everyone moving as far away as they could, making my family look as though they had something contagious!

Before too long they couldn't stand it either, so after a hurried picnic, the day was cut short, and with much relief to all concerned, we made a premature exit. I wasn't at all sorry never to be taken there again, being left at home to sleep and relax whenever the family returned there.

Another interesting beach, but much more suited to my needs, was Instow, with its long expanse of sand coupled together with dunes and shallow, friendly pools. However, not all the pools were shallow and friendly, and one such unfriendly pool changed my views somewhat, commanding more respect from me in the future.

While indulging in high speed runs across the sands, only two things would distract me from my arrow like path. One was Children, these delightful beings drawing me towards them like a magnet with their contagious clamouring. They were not always pleased to see me, perhaps the sight of a Red Arrow approaching at close on 30 mph. was too much, but they need not have worried as my last minute swerving was now perfected! The second was the pools. How refreshing to speed through them, cooling my undercar-

With the family at Instow

riage with refreshing spray, launch myself into the middle of one, or simply lay down and relax, sending bubbles cascading to the surface from my submerged nose.

On one occasion I had noticed someone standing beside an especially inviting pool and immediately changed direction to arrive at its edge at full tilt. I *had* noticed that it was bigger than average, but even as I flew gracefully through the air, I was not expecting the shock I got on hitting the water.

Pools were usually about a foot deep at the most, but when I hit the water this time, I completely disappeared and continued to drop like a stone to the bottom.

After what seemed an eternity, I burst back into the sunshine, my paws thrashing wildly as I tried desperately to rid myself of that sinking feeling. Tuning in to Dad's anxious voice, I quickly became very skilled at doggy paddle, but still managed a look of terror as I made clumsy progress towards the bank.

Only then did I see the man again, who had collapsed with laughter as he witnessed the whole action, his own Retriever dog having suffered the same fate only minutes earlier.

My most exciting and meritorious experience by the sea took place at Braunton Burrows and deserves special description.

It is most fitting then, with the Burrows being my favourite place of exercise, that such an intriguing adventure should take place there.

Normal activities deserve special mention, for the whole family shared my enthusiasm to such an extent as to lose ourselves among the dunes. So deep would be our penetration into the very heart of the area, that we would often return after the sun had departed, the fading light casting creepy shadows across the paths.

These were walks in the true sense of the word, there never being a dull moment, the interest provided being perfect for a make of dog such as me.

The combination was endless, country smells, wide open sandy spaces, thick undergrowth hiding invisible tenants, and the many ponds with their unique brand of watery entertainment. In summer this was the welcome coolness, but turned to excitement as mid Winter froze the surface to send me skating, legs splayed, across to the other side.

The incident in question took place on a gloomy and wintry Sunday afternoon while on one of our longer excursions.

My pleasure was obvious, as with saliva dripping freely from my lounging tongue, I followed countless rabbit smells, and disturbed many nesting birds, before descending into an isolated valley where events began.

I was half way across before I saw the tent, but being a similar colour to the surrounding bushes, was lucky to spot it at all. The suddenness of my discovery unnerved me, and I stopped in my tracks to lift a paw and point, coat bristling, while I worked out what to do next.

My nose won the struggle with my head, and inching forward, I had just reached the opening when the sight of a dirty, very unfriendly face popping out had me scampering back to more friendly company.

I had time only to notice his clothes were the same colour as the tent, before we changed course and headed for the car, no wonder I had not noticed him until the last moment

Getting lost had its disadvantages, for while we had plenty of time no one worried how long we took to find the homeward trail, but when we wanted the way out quickly, the sense of urgency even found its way down to my level.

As if that wasn't enough to worry about, I now spotted several pairs of legs at the top of a dune, and with the girls recognising them as belonging to Soldiers, I followed them up for a closer look. I'd never seen any before, but if these were anything to go by, then I certainly didn't want to meet any more!

Katie and Lyndsey may have thought it was all a game, but I for one didn't like the look of those menacing guns.

Well I didn't get shot obviously, but the amount of sand thrown in my direction was enough to halt my advance, so I set about barking at them instead. The girls were no longer amused and had returned to Mum, while I now responded readily to Dad's urgent whistling as the desire to be clear of the area was now shared by one and all!

According to Dad, we were clearly in the middle of an Army manoeuvre, and somewhere amongst the wilderness would be a second set of soldiers. As we quickened our pace towards the car park, and hopefully away from these unfriendly figures, we found ourselves passing through much thicker undergrowth, and with daylight distinctly fading, long sinister shadows now criss crossed our path.

I was now beginning to lose interest in the trail smells, electing to stay close to the Family, and it was probably this reason that allowed us to pass half the second group of Soldiers without realising they were there. What a creepy feeling. I didn't see them, I sensed them, but when Dad noticed my hackles standing erect, and my classic hunting pose, he most definitely saw them. We had been walking literally *inches* from their noses, for they were concealed among the bushes by our own feet, remaining undetected from even my acute senses.

I had the highest admiration for their animal skills, and how clever, I thought, for bringing the game down to my level, and wriggling forward I did my best to clean up the nearest dirty face.

This second group were as unsporting as the first, and once more I was abruptly given the cold shoulder, so I opened up again with my barks in reply.

As my barks vibrated through the chilly evening air, this proved to be the last straw, and we retreated at the double, as poor Dad conjured up visions of the Army War Games being brought to a premature halt by a Red Setter discovering a group of Soldiers who had otherwise remained undercover for the whole weekend.

We didn't wait for the outcome, quickly finding the car, and being more than happy to leave the burrows behind us, not surprisingly allowing a fair period of time before we returned, but making doubly sure never to wander that deep into the Dunes again.

There was one small consolation for me though, because in the girls' eyes I was the hero of the day, and they were quite proud of me, which, I suppose went some way to make up for the time at Lee Bay when I put a stop to their otherwise enjoyable day, and momentarily dropped to the bottom of their popularity ratings .

I think that more than anything was the worst punishment I could get.

Chapter Sixteen

Problems!

Everybody, whether animal or human, has their troubles, and my family was certainly no exception.

The earliest example I can recollect, was watching Dad reverse out of the garage, clip the gate and knock the wall down. What a noise, and what a splendid mess for me to sniff around in, happy in the knowledge that I had nothing at all to do with it!

There were numerous problems with the little white car, seemingly something would go wrong every week, and as well as causing the family many problems and headaches, this posed a serious threat to my walks. I was relieved then, when it was replaced by a much smarter, and altogether more reliable car.

Dad had excelled himself this time, completely ignoring the family's money problems to bring home a fine, green car, known as a Cortina G.T. The G.T. badge, I was told, was worthy of my name, and indeed, sitting in the front seat, gazing through all that glass and with all that space around me, I now knew how Shamus must feel on his outings. Even the winkers were so much better, and there was certainly no way they were going to switched on without my knowing.

Certainly I felt proud when left in the car, peering majestically down my nose at anyone daring to stop alongside, but unfortunately such ecstasy couldn't last, and with the Girls growing rapidly, I found myself on the front floor again.

Back came the frustrations for I needed to see through the windscreen to check that we were heading in the right direction.

This car was to be the last change to the family vehicles, Dad being especially pleased because there was little work to do on it, and obviously I was only too thankful to continue my trips to and from my favourite haunts.

There were problems in which I could play my part, such as keeping the back garden safe for our feathered friends and allowing them somewhere secure to eat their food and rest tired wings. This I did by chasing the cats away, a task I undertook with great relish, for I never did trust an animal which arched its back like a camel, and hissed like a kettle.

My perseverance with the cats now proved doubly worthwhile when the back garden became sanctuary for an injured seagull.

I discovered this unlucky bird during one of my regular walks over the field, having no difficulty at all in tracing his painful squawks, or tracking down the wretched fellow, for he had been shot through the wing

That Seagull

Once safe in the confines of our garden, he soon made himself at home, taking a special interest in the rockery and making it his roost, no doubt likening it to the cliffs by the sea.

Although he could still be easily caught at feeding times, that wicked looking hooked beak was still causing many problems. Dad suffered from scarred hands, while my nose came in for a fair amount of pecking but nevertheless, our feathered visitor was the centre of attraction, especially with the girls who took a keen interest and helped me out on my cat patrol

For a few days then, I was kept busy padding around, watching intently at feeding times, while our seagull friend became part or the garden and I developed quite a fondness for him.

Eventually my patrols (and my nose) were relieved by the arrival of an Animal Doctor who took the poor little fellow away to a Bird Hospital.

Problems, at times would bring out different conditions in me, as described in the following examples:

1. Fright

While I was alone in the bungalow, Dad came home from town without his keys and had to break in.

On hearing noises from one of the bedrooms, I gave out the quietest of token barks, hoping dearly that the intruder would hurry up and go away. In fact I really thought I had succeeded when the bungalow returned to its normal stillness. How wrong could I be?

To my dismay, I heard footsteps in the bedroom and retreated hurriedly into a dark corner to hide. From my corner, the sight of a shadowy figure moving down the Hallway sent the familiar shivers sweeping through my body, followed by a flood of high pitched yaps involuntarily rolling out so rapidly, that they eventually spilled over into one long, frightened howl. What a relief to find out it was only Dad, and while he gave me an understanding welcome to bring my pulse rate down, I tip toed into the bedroom to find out just how he had managed it.

He entered the House that way several times after that, but every single time it would scare the living daylights out of me, and each time I wondered how I could possibly stand it, I'm sure the carpet couldn't !

2. Pain

When my tail got sucked up by the Vacuum Cleaner.

I never did like that noisy thing anyway, but I suppose I became too complacent on the day it happened.

On hearing that detestable howl getting nearer, I would move pretty smartly out of the way, but on that hot summer's day, I just couldn't be bothered, and paid the price for my laziness by allowing the machine to roll over my tail.

With a whoosh, my pride and joy disappeared up inside, and try as I might, couldn't do anything about getting it back.

Thinking that the rest of me would follow, I squealed out in panic, my terrified yelps actually drowning the noise from the cleaner. Heaven knows what people down the Avenue must have thought, but after what seemed an age, the noise finally stopped. My beautiful tail was unravelled and gently retrieved from the insides of the dreadful monster and very carefully examined by Mum, whose concern easily matched mine, but amazingly the damage was only slight.

Even so, on future cleaning sessions, I took no chances, and as soon as the fearful noise hammered through the bungalow, I claimed the security of my bed just as quickly as was possible.

Incidentally that wasn't the first time my tail became the target for abuse because, back in the days of our white Car, it got squashed in the door while we were visiting Instow.

Dad had seemed to put everything into slamming the door, while I added to the injury by trying to gallop at my usual pace. Everyone on the sea front must have heard my squeals that day!

3. Discomfort

When, after rolling in some especially smelly and interesting sheep mess I was taken home for another bath.

No need to rewrite my comments on that subject, but this time there was a shower to increase my discomfort. Not only did I have to contend with the task of keeping my balance, but now I had the equivalent of a torrential downpour over me, and the final indignity was the girls' bubbly shampoo.

Whatever will humans think of next, to rub syrup into me and produce more bubbles and lather than I'd ever seen before. Now if

I had come home in that condition there would there would have been trouble!

At least I had the consolation to round off the proceedings under the hairdryer, but the combination of warm air and soft perfumed fur resulted in a very curly, smelly, Red Setter.

I certainly wouldn't let Shamus see me in such a condition, and what that rotten black poodle down the road would have done, just didn't bear thinking about. The immediate problem was how to get by the nosy creature without being noticed, because I just couldn't wait to get out of this poofy condition by visiting the field as soon as possible, and roll in some decent smelling mess again !

4. Comfort

The day a road sweeper lorry tried to sweep our green car up with the rubbish:

What a mess that made of it, and what a noise, everyone for several streets around must have heard it, yet when poor Mum went out to try and sort things out, not one person came to her assistance. The only help she was going to get was four legged; I pressed hard up against her legs as a reminder that this was one best friend who could be relied on for help and comfort whenever the need arose.

Once the bully lorry had departed and Mum had sunk into a soft chair, I needed to summon all my skills as a comforter, but as I pressed my face harder and still harder against hers, the gentle stroke of a hand down my back showed my efforts were at least worthwhile.

5. Stress

When I became so worked up, that I put my rear quarters through the glass front door.

It didn't take too much to get me going, the smallest excitement being plenty to set me off, but on this occasion, Nana Polly really set the proceedings swinging.

She had come up to the bungalow to join us for a walk to the Burrows, but in her eagerness to include me into the proceedings, had raised my excitement up to a frenzy. The big crunch came when the porch door was opened during a manoeuvre usually timed to perfection.

At the very first signs of departure, I would press myself firmly against the door, making it totally impossible to be prised open without my squeezing through first. With the door finally open, after a struggle I was able to bound forward to within a couple of feet from the front door before my paws actually touched the floor for the first time and then spin round to land with my bottom pressed hard up against the front door glass.

The result of this acrobatic movement was that no one could leave the bungalow before me. There was simply no way I was going to be left behind.

On this occasion though, such was the excitement, that once the porch door was prised open enough to release me, I flew through the air at twice my normal rate, spinning round at high speed to land with a tremendous crash against the glass. The result being that my rear end went straight through, so that I was half in and half out of the Bungalow.

Everybody rushed to rescue this poor, bewildered heap stuck through the glass, everyone except Dad that is, because he was furious. And how! Picking me up and hurling me back into the bungalow without even bothering to check if I was injured or not.

'No walk for you, you *swine*,' he bellowed.

Nana Polly looked equally guilty as we all returned to the hall, but I'm glad to say that after all the mess had been cleared up, and I had been pronounced free from injury Dad had relented enough to allow me back into the car.

There were times when problems meant drastic changes to the family routine.

I was caught well and truly on the hop, just as I had settled into a further day's holiday, smack, bang in the middle of it, Dad actually went off to work. What sort of shift was this for goodness sake?

Dad stayed away till long after the television had been switched off and the bungalow was plunged into darkness.

When I say darkness, I mean just that, because I followed Mum around, watching intrigued, as she lit one candle after another, simply assuming that it was all part of the Christmas decorations.

That theory was snuffed out just as quickly as the lights themselves, and those pretty candles certainly provided a friendly glow, but I couldn't work out how Mum knew it was all going to happen.

The Power Cuts seemed to go on for ages with me, Mum and the girls all huddled up together for company.

At least on normal night shifts we had the lights to help us through, and provide a certain amount of protection against the night noises. The girls were lucky again, having no trouble getting off to sleep, while Mum only had her radio for company, and, I'm glad to say, my trips out to the garden were carefully selected before the lights went out.

This crazy state of affairs continued every other day, but if I thought that was bad then I was surely in for a shock as worse was to come the following week. That really finished me, because, as we all sat close together, watching the flickering shadows on the walls, I waited patiently for the family to make a move to go to bed. At last preparations started, or so I thought, because my relief turned to utter confusion when I realised Dad was actually preparing to go to work! Can you imagine that? Midnight, straining to keep awake, and sets off to work.

I was beginning to give up trying to understand my family at all, because not only did Dad leave us in the middle of the night, but didn't put in a reappearance until the following mid day, when he promptly went off to bed.

No, I certainly couldn't keep up with all that, I knew the family had strange habits, but mixing up Night Shift, Day Shift, and Holidays, combined with the spooky power cuts, was most unsettling, and this stupid system was to continue for the rest of the winter.

I can't describe how relieved we all were when things returned to some of sanity in the spring, while I agreed that the strange and nonsensical period, was definitely the longest we could remember, and one we all would love to forget.

That change in routine though, was nothing compared to the bombshell dropped on the family a couple of years later.

It was during the autumn. Time was passing smoothly, my only concern being that the shortening days meant a threat to my evening walks.

On the day in question, I was wondering about the likelihood of a walk when Dad came in, bringing such an atmosphere of gloom with him that I spotted it immediately, forgot about such mundane things as walks and kept close to him to be ready to offer what help I could.

Dad had lost his job, that much I understood, but apart from the grim faces around me, I couldn't begin to understand how serious the situation was. No job obviously meant no money, and I heard tales of how some of Dad's friends had to cut back so much, it meant goodbye to their pets.

Thankfully, such problems were not for my head, and the family considered no such cut backs, but even as they discussed a rather bleak future, fortune was to smile on them before the week was out.

A new job had been found in Barnstaple, Dad doing well to get himself fixed up so quickly, and start immediately.

This good news following on the heels of such bad news had the effect of lifting the crestfallen look, and put some sparkle back into the family.

Few people could have understood my ways like Mum and Dad, but being a local job it not only cut out those dreadful extended trips to and from work, but was to bring many welcome changes to my routine.

Chapter Seventeen

Changes

The make up of a Red Setter is such that any change which takes place no matter how small, or how large, will receive equal meticulous attention, from a tiny flower being brought into the bungalow, to the problems of adapting to a completely new routine.

The new job certainly brought its share of changes, but all good ones I'm very pleased to say.

For a start, I was taken there one lunch time in the old Rover, had a Visitors' badge attached to my collar, and went on a tour of the Factory. I saw where Dad spent his days and, best of all, was introduced to many of his workmates, most of whom actually liked me!

After the tour, I was taken back to the car and commanded to stay quietly there all afternoon. I certainly didn't mind that, the weather was cool and I knew very well Dad would return before he could drive home.

Even without trying, I became the centre of attraction just by being there. Sitting bolt upright as I often did to keep an eye on any movement, I liked to keep my back pushed hard against the seat, and to do this I pushed my paws equally hard against the steering wheel.

This position of mine so intrigued a workmate known as "The Major" that he hurried back inside to enquire if Dad had the keys, because if not, the car was likely to be driven away at any moment. Don't think I couldn't either; I watched *everything* that went on from driving to cooking and knew exactly what to do and when to do it!

The most exciting change concerned with the new job, was Mum learning to drive. This meant more outings for me, plus the occasional trip to the factory at lunch time for a walk in the adjoining field.

The days were certainly not so long now, but regrettably I still couldn't relax even though I had most of the car to myself, perhaps I would never be satisfied until I got to drive!

At least the changes came at a rate which allowed me to examine and adjust to each and every one, and therefore, even the most insignificant change came in for the closest scrutiny.

For instance, there was the arrival, early on in my life, of the front room carpet. Probably of little interest to many pets, and possibly boring to the reader, but all the same, after being used to bare boards for a couple of years, it came in for close inspection from me, its soft deep pile being luxury to walk and lie on. Now, of course, large patches are wearing thin due to my mad circular movements.

Then there was the arrival of the first street light, bang outside the gate, improving my late night outings into the garden no end. Instead of a quick dash to the nearest patch of grass in pitch darkness, I could afford a casual sniff around, feeling most relaxed under the gentle glow of the lamp. Far too casual sometimes, because, so interested would I become in the garden or else sit down on the path to gaze out through the gate, that I would quite forget the original reason for going out.

By the time I had been reminded by my tummy, Dad would be asleep, and, not wanting to wet the floor meant waking him up, not the most pleasant of jobs, I can assure you.

Some changes actually improved my welfare. A fine example being the arrival of the girls' beds, which, being fairly high off the floor, meant less of me on show to those pesky wasps when I took refuge there.

There again, some changes lowered my standard of living, as proved by the arrival of a bigger settee, and my prime position on the end of the old one was immediately banned. That quite upset me, for one reason the bigger settee was not even new, and for another, I had got really used to my own place by the window, an excellent position from which I could easily stretch my head to glance through it, thus keeping activities under control while remaining warm and comfortable inside. None of the family would dare sit in my space, and if anyone should take up too much room, I would squeeze myself hard against the arm of the settee and push the offending person away with my paws outstretched.

Even though my blanket was laid in front of the fire, I continually tried to ease my way back on, but even my silkiest of moves were foiled, and without so much as an apology, found myself returned to the floor forthwith.

There were times though, when Mum relented in spite of Dad's disapproving warnings of being spoilt, and I would be lifted onto her lap to be cuddled like a baby, the fact that I was twice the size of one not even being considered. If that was being spoilt, then I didn't mind one bit, loving every moment, lapping up the stroking, having my paws tickled, and never failing to lengthen my stay by flashing plenty of large Brown and very sad eyes.

Before Lyndsey was moved into her own bedroom, it used to be a a store room, a right mess, full of interesting smells and objects. It was into this room that Dad continually disappeared at odd times for a number of years, yes, *years*! Week after week sawing, filing and generally increasing the amount of mess in there, and without getting told off once!

The outcome of all this activity resulted in some worktops and cabinets for the kitchen. The table (Dad called it a *breakfast bar*) was just right for me. I could curl up underneath it, snug against the wall, or sit with my head resting on Mum's knees, being ideally positioned for any tit bits coming my way. Whenever a meal was imminent I would squirm in between the legs as fast as I could, being well in position long before anyone had finished sitting down.

Another of Dad's do-it-yourself episodes, resulted in a fine wooden box for me, varnish finish all over and sprung floor included, fitting neatly beside the Hall door to provide me with my very own corner, with Mum adding red curtains along the glass partition to complete the effect.

Turning round in my box would mean getting tangled up in the curtains more often than not, so that I disappeared from view until woken up, but all this only added to the comfort, making my corner a cosy one indeed.

Changes in routine were the hardest to adjust to, too much for my brain to take in all in one go, but more so when they involved the girls.

Obviously they couldn't stay young forever, just because I never grew up, didn't necessarily mean that they could get away with it, so eventually the day came when Katie went off to playschool.

That day was bad enough, wondering how she would get on without me on hand to keep an eye on her, leaving me at home, unsettled until she returned, but when Lyndsey joined her a short time later, I had to rearrange my day dramatically, fearing that Mum may be the next to disappear and leave me on my own again. Happily that didn't quite happen, there even being the bonus of an extra walk when accompanying the Girls to playschool and home again. I still pulled on the lead all the way there and back again. but I did enjoy them nevertheless.

On one particular day a change occurred that frightened the living day lights out of me.

Half way along the route was a bridge, all it had ever meant to me was just a wall, I didn't recognise it as a bridge until the day a footbridge was built alongside and away from the traffic.

A very good idea for the girls of course, but I was half way across the thing when I realised the side was only covered with wire mesh allowing me a distinct view of the ground a long way below, and back came that old feeling in my legs.

The only way I could bring myself to cross was to get down on my tummy again and creep along, even though there was still the pavement beneath my paws. Happily we always kept to the other side of the road on future trips.

On Katie's Birthday, not only routine changed, but family life as well, for amongst her presents that day, there came into the Bungalow of all things ... a Bird!

I had always been taught to have great respect for our feathered friends, with my excellent job keeping cats away from the garden, trying hard not to disturb the little creatures while they fed, but this bundle of squawking blue feathers looked like staking a claim on some of the affection usually reserved for me. Katie and Lyndsey, I didn't mind coming second to, but a *Budgie*? Never! The family even started talking to the pesky thing, teaching it to fly and talk, *talk*! Something as small as that chirping 'Pretty Boy' all day was really going to get right up my nose.

First of all I kept away, keeping my distance and trying to ignore it, but she insisted on flapping down, arriving at full speed and causing me great inconvenience by having to violently duck my head in order not to be dive-bombed and therefore completely unsettling me. I hated the flapping of its wings while it was in the air, and equally hated the thought of stepping on it when it was on the floor.

The family were particularly amused to watch me tip-toeing around as if the floor was red hot, hardly daring to put my paws down, or slinking off to the safety of my box, seemingly chased off by something no bigger than my paw.

Although I couldn't stand the bird, the last thing I wanted was to damage it, but it was definitely pushing its luck during those low flights across the room on a collision course with my head and needed teaching a lesson pretty quickly! I would therefore open my mouth wide, snapping my jaws shut with a crash the moment it passed through, purely as a reminder as to who was the real boss.

The next Christmas, the "Budgie Brigade" became two, with the arrival of a bigger green bird, but this one was only here for a short time, and strangely enough, I developed a great affection for him.

The moment his cage descended onto the table, any dislike for this pet invading my domain disappeared when I had a very strong feeling that all was not well. He had been injured at some time and couldn't fly, so the thought of a crippled budgie prompted me to take on the task of guardian.

I would lay for hours beside his cage, or just sit beside him when the little fellow was allowed out, allowing him to pick over my fur and generally making him feel wanted and at home.

His holiday with us then was far too short, and it was a great shame to see the friendly bird go as I'd become quite attached to him, wondering just how he would fare without me,

So I resigned myself to more bombing runs from Katie's budgie, now given the absurd name of "Wings", (at least the big green fellow had the masculine name of "Hercules"). In spite of all her faults though, I must have had some feeling for the little bird, becoming most concerned when Dad put on a black glove, and attacked her with a pair of scissors. It was only for a claw trimming session I'm relieved to say, but at least Wings could depend on me if it ever came to the crunch.

That pesky budgie!

By now I felt that I could adjust to any change, whether good or bad, but, experienced as I was, there was still the odd change that would leave me thoroughly confused.

There was the time, for instance, when several workmen took out all the windows, including my partition, only to put some more back in again

I couldn't work out the sense in that at all. Dad called it "Double Glazing". It made little difference to me, but I was informed on very good authority while I was sniffing the new windows earnestly trying to find something different, that my corner would now be warmer, and that was always good news to me!

Then, more recently, we had something called a "Phone" installed. That really annoyed me!

First of all, I had my bed removed for some workmen to fit the thing just above my bed, that was an invasion of my privacy for a start! Then the blasted contraption developed the unsettling habit of producing an awful bleeping sound just as I seemed to be relaxing, almost turning my ears inside out.

The final insult though would be Mum leaving whatever she was doing to hurry over to answer the thing every time that irritating noise wailed, as if it was some kind of God, impatient to be attended to, and demanding immediate attention day or night.

I would become so uptight at Mum talking to a blue "Bone" as if her very life depended on it, that I would bark my disapproval, getting myself hastily pushed into the front room as a result. Little wonder then, that I developed a dislike for that as well. At other times, the phone would be thrust under my ear flap to listen to a tiny far off version of Dad's voice, and became yet another item to add to my list of objects to flash the whites of my eyes at.

While that was one change I could have well done without, there occurred at the same time, a really big change that I whole heartedly approved of.

Just one workman descended on us, staying for a whole week, but although he was only one, he certainly created chaos during his entire stay. Carpets and floorboards were taken up, holes driven through walls, (more mess incidentally, than I had created in my entire naughty moments added together!) Long pipes were buried under the floor boards in the very best bone-hiding fashion, but most important, smooth white radiators were hung with the utmost precision upon the walls.

'Very pretty,' I thought, 'I only hope *they* don't start bleeping!'

I soon got my answer. While laying in my box, my delicate senses picked up a gentle tinkling noise.

Hunting around, my search brought me to the smooth white radiator opposite to my bed, and it now came in for a great amount of poking. The more I poked, the hotter it became, until it was far too hot for my nose, but not too hot for my body! Stretching out along the bottom of the radiator, I could happily have one side of me warmed up without any damage of singeing, or even blocking anyone else's heat.

I soon worked out the times to lie alongside, or, should I lose track of the times, I could lie in my box and await the start of the tinkling sound. My own apartment was now complete!

I mentioned that the heating was put in at the same time as the phone, I've also mentioned that visitors were rare, but on one rainy day, everyone in Barnstaple seemed to arrive!

Outside there were large yellow vans, small white vans and cars, while inside were electrical men, gas men, Buzby men (Dad's joke) and our own friendly workman, all stepping over each other, cursing, not only me, but themselves as well.

I don't know about them, but I had a great time, welcoming everyone in turn and keeping an eye on them all by rushing from room to room, twisting myself in half, and even going as far as dropping a little "welcome wee" and it was some time since I had got *that* excited!

I got a fairly good reception even if I did get tangled up in some wire, chase off with the odd screwdriver, or dip my paw in one or two cups of tea! Still, I was the sort of animal who insisted on knowing everything that was happening, and knowing that it was being done properly.

The last development at this time was Mum going back to a part time job after many years of trying, but with me set up in my new comfort, who was I to complain, in any case it was only every other morning.

This didn't bother me nearly as much as before, I was quite happy tucked up in my double glazed, carpeted, and centrally heated apartment, and was more than content with my lot.

With Katie and Lyndsey

Chapter Eighteen

Down on The Farm

As well as improvements in my routine, we all benefited from the increase in friends as Dad settled into his new job, and an increase in friends naturally led to an increase in interesting visits.

One such visit deserves singling out for special description, and although starting off very mundane, developed into a most rewarding and entertaining event.

It was getting towards the end of winter, but instead of the weather becoming gradually warmer, the temperature dropped considerably as we endured a spell of most un-spring-like weather.

Nevertheless, on a cold, grey, Sunday morning, we called at Wynsum to collect Nana Polly, and set off for the Moors.

This of course, was the boring part, and as we progressed deeper into moorland, I became increasingly agitated, my degree of restlessness being measured by the number of slimy marks on the windscreen from my incessant prodding.

Little wonder really, my longest trip for a visit out towards the Moors was to call on a most friendly couple at Loxhore, who were friends of Dad's from long ago, even far beyond pre-Setter days, explained Dad.

Before we had travelled very much further, the grey skies opened up and started shedding tiny white, fluffy tufts, which skated tantalisingly across the windscreen, and occupied my attention for a while. When this ceased to be a novelty, I became restless again, and this time Dad lost his cool.

Losing his way didn't help matters either, and as we skated to and fro through the Exmoor lanes, I inevitably took the blame.

As the moors began to turn magically into a Christmas Card picture, Dad at last found the turning he had been desperately searching for, and hearing the winkers clicking away, I eagerly readied myself for an introduction to the snow sailing lazily but steadily past the windows.

With Katie and Lyndsey safely protected from my excited paws, I was propelled out into the wintry scene. The snow had settled to the depth of my paw, and I loved the way it crunched and compressed with every step. Slippery too, that was exciting, but while playing happily in this new and interesting substance, I had not noticed the family moving over to the farm house, becoming momentarily alarmed to find myself alone in a strange place.

Panicking, I completely forgot how slippery the ground had now become, and consequently, had little control of my movement across the yard, almost squashing the girls against the door as I cannoned into them.

Dad's friend invited us, yes me included, into the house, and what a house! Being a farm house it was huge, but what really took my attention was the state of it. A *shambles*, just up my street, no wonder I was allowed in. There were clothes strewn about all over the place, toys and objects dotted around, cushions on the floor, in fact just the sort of place for me to have a good sniff. If I was delighted, Mum was amazed, her face a picture as she surveyed the scene because the few essentials we owned were always immaculately placed, and I don't think she could believe her own eyes.

Within a couple of minutes I had found two cats to play with, and then I couldn't believe my eyes, when down the stairs hopped of all things a *rabbit*. No hurry, it was just calmly hopping down the stairs and wandering quietly into the kitchen ignoring us completely. Under normal circumstances, the sight of such an animal would have me charging off for a game, but for once I was completely barkless, and simply sat and watched the bobtail until out of sight.

This was going to be a den of surprises, that was for sure, and after everyone had been given refreshments, we moved outside.

David, our well spoken host, proceeded to proudly show us around his animal collection, and here I was to meet many new members of the animal kingdom. Half expecting the inevitable command to return to the car, I walked quietly beside Dad, but as we reached the sheds, and no such command had been made, I started to look forward to meeting the different animals.

I wouldn't have missed the experience for the world. For a start, wandering about the courtyard were a strange mixture of feathered folk. There were chickens, ducks, turkeys and geese. I kept well away from the latter, not liking in the least the way they stretched their necks high in the air, flapped their wings strongly and hissed angrily.

On arriving at the sheds I was still in tow, behaving myself impeccably, and, peering through a convenient crack, I gazed at some cows, happy in the knowledge that I was indeed safe from their horns. I loved the calves at the far end though. We were then introduced to the two large horses which were the much-loved and personal possession of David and his wife, before setting off to see the animals for which this trip was all about.

Here at last came the command to keep my distance, but I did manage to get a glimpse of the occupants of the shed nearest to the farm house.

Sheep! Those elusive creatures I could only view from a very discreet distance, but outnumbering the sheep, were newborn lambs, every inch like the cuddly toys the girls played with at home.

Not even the Family were allowed in there, because David explained carefully in his posh voice, that if a newborn lamb is touched by a Human, then the mother would quite possibly reject it. Imagine what the mother would have done if her lambs were sniffed by a Red Setter!

We all gazed at these cute little creatures for ages, the girls just longing to cuddle them, and me? Well, I'm sure my maternal instincts would have seen me through. We were allowed a close up of the older lambs and the girls got their cuddles in before David and Dad set off up the hill to check on the sheep and any more newborn lambs.

The rest of us moved back into the warmth of the farm house for more welcome refreshments, leaving as we did so, a thick trail of mud along the floor, and I waited for the complaints. When there were none, I began to feel more relaxed by the minute, feeling quite at home by the time we arrived in a cosy wooden room, with a very low ceiling, supported by large black beams. I gazed around at this unusual room for a long time wondering how Dad would fare with his height, but I felt sure, if I jumped up, reaching the beams would be just as easy for me.

Several people sat around a large table, and while the family were invited to join them, I made my way towards a glorious, roaring fire.

To start with I didn't think I was going to get too close, because laying in front were two large farm dogs, but like everyone else on the farm, were super friendly, and didn't mind in the least having a strange dog share their heat.

By the time Dad returned the folk around the table were having a fine old time with the sound of chatter, plus the occasional song penetrating my sleepy ears as I lazily toasted myself in front of the crackling flames. My fears for Dad's head were indeed well founded when a dull thud, followed by a discreet curse indicated with little surprise to me that his head was far too high for the old black beams. What did surprise me though was the continuing friendship extended to me by the farm dogs by allowing me to share in the tit bits thrown down from the table.

The party broke up when David invited my family to fill up some bottles with homemade wine, while his two daughters appeared on the scene to lead Katie and Lyndsey towards the Nursery. I naturally followed my charges, tearing myself away from the fire with a certain amount of reluctance, and escorting them into the Nursery where we came upon the final surprise.

Toys of all shapes, sizes and description, both hard and soft, were piled roof high, and the girls were the ones to stand and stare this time. Following the example of Gemma and Sacha, they set about the toys with great enthusiasm even thumping away at a full size piano, but nobody minded in the least.

Katie and Lyndsey played for ages, each lost in their own private world of make believe, while David's Girls seemed only too pleased for the company on such a bleak day. I set about sorting through the piles with equal enthusiasm, and all too soon we were required to withdraw from the delightful place.

Without exception then, we were all extremely loath to leave such a hospitable home. Nevertheless we made our way reluctantly to-wards the car, to bid farewell to our generous friends and set off through the deepening snow.

I hadn't experienced snow quite like that before, my only former experience being the very watery variety, and was looking forward to a game with the girls when we arrived home.

Unfortunately, all there was in Barnstaple was a lot of cold water, the only snow in sight clinging to the car, and I reflected on the disadvantages of being so far from the Moors ... for me that was !

Chapter Nineteen

My Average Day

Anyone who has the mistaken idea that a day in the life of a dog must be a pretty boring affair, should give the matter some more thought, and to anyone who would write us off in this fashion, please allow me to put the matter right by running through my average day.

Of course, to the genuine dog lover who knows a thing or two about how we can become accepted members of the household by offering the family so much affection, trust and companionship in return for our keep, my average day will hold few surprises.

With such a comfortable, interior sprung box to sleep in, surrounded by all my super "Mod Cons"; Double Glazing, curtain, carpet, and radiator, I was in no hurry to leave such a cosy corner first thing in the morning.

However, I had long since learned the importance of Dad's work. So when the sound of his radio drifted down the hall long enough to penetrate my dreams, I would stretch each leg in turn before dragging myself out to stretch, firstly my front end, and then my rear, ending up by collapsing in an exhausted heap on the floor.

By now I'd be awake enough to casually wander along the hall, into the Bedroom and round to the far side of the bed to poke Dad continually with my cold, wet nose to stop him dropping off to sleep again.

His difficulty at achieving the task of rising from the bed was equal to mine, so without my timely intervention, heaven knows what time he would have put in an appearance.

Once a week, there would be no radio, this day I soon learned to be Sunday. Nothing and no one stirred until I woke up, but instead of poking Dad this time, I was most careful to stop at Mum's side of the bed, prodding gently before laying my head over her neck until there were signs of movement.

Back to the weekdays now, and once satisfied that my early morning mission had been successfully accomplished, I sauntered along to the front door to be let out. After the long night, I was only too eager to go, which would be just great when the weather was fine.

I tried the gate naturally, this being a habit never to be broken, in fact, I never particularly wanted to try, and if my luck was in, I could sneak a visit to the field, having the whole area to myself, unless joined for my early morning ramble by my friend Monty.

In spite of all the luxury of fresh dewy smells reserved exclusively for me to savour, I made sure that I didn't stay too long. For one reason I naturally didn't want the secret of the unlocked gate to become known, while the other reason was simply that Dad left himself very little time after staggering out of bed to get off to work, and should he have to come searching for me as well, then I most certainly would be in big trouble.

I did catch myself out once. While putting out the milk bottles, Dad found the gate open, and thinking I was in the back garden, latched it quickly in a vain effort to stop me getting out. Of course, I was already over the field, and on returning, found myself in the embarrassing position of having to bark in order to get back into the garden. Fortunately Dad saw the funny side of that situation!

If the gate was shut, I would often just sit and stare down the road to dream of the field, or search for unlikely signs of life.

Obviously, with such thoughts distracting me from my main errand, I would quite forget to wee again, having to ask when my tummy reminded me of my absentmindedness when back inside, and earning some more black looks.

It was a totally different matter in the wet though, and I would tiptoe onto the grass to curtsy precariously on three legs with my rear end as far possible above the grass, before hurrying back to the front door, and yapping plaintively until let in to the warmth and comfort of the house.

I didn't return to my bed though, but made straight for the kitchen cupboard, getting in everybody's way, or generally attracting attention to myself until presented with my favourite breakfast, a Bonio.

Every day without fail I would carry this treasured possession back to my bed, where I could get away with laying my rear end on the carpet as long as the more important crumbly end was on my bed. Once this exact position had been carefully selected, I would hold the delightful and crispy biscuit between my paws, chewing away slowly and deliberately, so that I could enjoy every mouthful without wasting a single crumb, and should the unlikely occurrence take place, then the offending crumbs would fall safely onto my bed, to be sniffed up at my leisure.

My next move would be well anticipated, and as I made my way towards the front room door, I seldom had time enough to sit down before it was magically opened to allow me access to the settee (before the ban!) to finish off my sleep now that all the morning tasks had been completed. All except one, that is, for I could never relax completely until Dad had been finally dispatched to work.

Occasionally, on a weekend, the family would set off for a trip, and being fairly lengthy, it was impossible for me to go along. All was not lost however, for I would benefit from the bonus of an official walk over the field.

How I enjoyed those. The warm, early morning sun, gently shining down, and the grass soaked with sweet-smelling and unspoilt dew soft under my paws.

The atmosphere was marvellous, the smells indescribable and super fresh as many wild animals were still out and about (if I was supposed to track them down, then no one had ever told me) while the sound of birds searching for some breakfast was almost deafening.

These walks were truly excellent, often taking in many fields, the family making sure I was fully exercised because they felt guilty about leaving me behind, even though, with my condition, taking me along would have been totally out of the question, and extremely nerve racking for all concerned, and in any case, after one of those long excursions, I was ready for a good rest.

Helping Mum shake my bed

If the long grass had made me too wet, I was made to run up and down the Avenue to dry off, well not so much made, as encouraged because it was a most enjoyable task and one into which I put a lot of effort, naturally leading to a fine display of barking, which in turn led to strong words from Mum. Since she often complained about the " lack of noise ", I really thought I was doing well to introduce some.

Back to my average day, and the turn of the girls to set off to school, momentarily leaving me with the bungalow all to myself, during which time I would note the arrival of the Milkman with a certain amount of suspicion, reserving my deepest barks for that occasion. I'm not sure why, perhaps it was that great black beard, but once he had gone, I could relax and look forward to Mum's return at any time.

This would involve a good deal of tail wagging and the few drops of "welcome wee" soaking slowly into the carpet would spark off a tour of housework. I would take a great deal of interest in all that followed, as I made a keen inspection of all work done, following closely from room to room, watching carefully every task carried out from bed making to washing clothes, extra interest being indicated by a wag of the tail whenever I came across clothes with a friendly smell on them.

I enjoyed the trip to the washing line, wasting no time in basking in the sunshine until following close on Mum's heels, we returned inside to set about preparing the lunch.

Sometimes I was called upon for assistance, one particularly enjoyable job was to help shake my blanket.

As soon as I witnessed it being removed from my box, I hurried eagerly out into the garden to grab one corner, and jumping up high on my hind legs, gave one end a most vigorous shaking while Mum held on tightly to the other. The enjoyment gained from this exercise being such that I would happily roll a growl with pleasure. Most enjoyable!

The cooking I would watch from a discreet distance, handily placed in the hall. From this safe position, I would not be under feet as I studied every single movement, while on the other paw, my position was ideal for any tit bit coming my way.

My two favourites were cheese and raw pastry, lumps of which were made available without fail, and also without fail, they would land inches from my nose, as after years of practice, they were tossed accurately in my direction by Mum, who took it all for granted, not even having to turn her head away from the work in hand!

On receiving a lump of, well, anything, I would readily pick it up and retreat swiftly to my box where, on dropping it safely in the middle of my blanket, I would turn my head around purely to check that it was really OK for me to eat it. Having satisfied myself on that score, I could settle down and set about devouring the morsel with great relish.

With the cooking finally completed, among the goodies retrieved from the oven would be a piece of pastry especially baked for me to eat later in the afternoon, and in return for this kind thought, I would again lift my head to eat it without spilling a single crumb onto the carpet.

The cooking of the Sunday dinner was a mouth-watering occasion for me, watching from my hall position, or leaning heavily against wall or radiator. (I would take the pressure off my legs or warm myself at every opportunity.)

When the Family were ready to move into the front room for dinner, I would take up a position under the table, usually alongside the girls. I told you I was intelligent, and this was just the place odd pieces, or more likely unwanted pieces, of dinner came my way, their secret was safe with me, and most of it was highly acceptable. With the dinner completed, I would follow the dinner plates out to the kitchen with my head held high, or prancing up and down like a rocking horse, but although this provided everyone with much amusement, I still had to wait until later for the scraps, having learnt long ago never to lick off the plates.

More amusement was provided during the first "Legal" offering.

This concerned the cream carton, which eventually came my way after the girls had finished arguing over which one was going to give it to me. The reason for all the fuss concerned the face I had to pull in order to get a grip on the flimsy container, having to pull the flanks of my mouth well back, baring my teeth like a savage beast while trying to reach my bed without spilling any of the precious contents.

The unfortunate, but only too regular, result from all this careful preparation being the container flipping back over my nose, leaving me with cream all over my face, and although this charade would take place every week, almost without fail, it continued to provide a great amount of amusement. Strange people, these humans.

Sunday afternoons have been well covered with the description of my walks, but I should add that my impatience to be first into the car didn't improve at all, and was only matched by my impatience to get out again once the walk was over.

The Bungalow being my one and only home, and the only place in which I could really relax, I was always eager to get back to it!

Leaping out of the car, I would move swiftly up to the front door to stand or lean impatiently until it was unlocked, then *whoosh*. Woe betide anyone foolish enough to try and beat me to it. When I got inside what was there to panic about? Even I couldn't work that one out, so I just relaxed and curled up in my box instead.

Weekday afternoons usually meant being in the garden if the weather was fine, and I took a great interest in the gardening, even though my "help" with the digging was never appreciated.

I could busy myself leaping and catching the midges, watching my "dog rocks" getting shovelled up and safely deposited in the dustbin, generally sniffing about or simply lazing in a warm sunny spot, anything really as long as I could provide some company. Such company would include a fair number of games, which was quite acceptable until I went too far, causing damage, and stirring Mum into action by chasing me around the bungalow with a broom. This action was usually a sobering one for me, because I could never make out whether she was joking or not, and noting the size of those heavy bristles, never felt like finding out!

Then of course, my company meant it was my turn to be on the receiving end of some more of Dad's tricks.

The classic one concerned a leaf or such like, which I would be completely unsure of, when it attracted my attention. Moving up to it in my slow motion style, with my back legs stretched way out behind, hackles up, whiskers out and concentration at its peak, Dad would leap out and scare the living daylights out of me.

Now for the big event of the afternoon, the arrival of Katie and Lyndsey home from school. I reserved a big welcome for them, and if the quiet part of my day was now over, then I didn't mind one little bit.

Occasionally some tiny friends came in with them, and I had to try extra hard to keep my natural exuberance at bay, putting on my softest Velvet Paws, but most times, I'm glad to say that I had them all to myself.

One incident brought out my protective instincts to such an extent, that it surprised even me.

Katie had just got out of the car when a boy a little bigger than her came running up, and clasping his arms around her, lifted my Charge clean off the ground. 'That can't be right,' I thought, and deftly leapt across to grab his trousers, shaking him violently until he let go. As it turned out, he was a friend, and as I licked him thoroughly from head to foot, was most happy to find there was no damage. Far from being angry, Dad was most impressed by my action and no doubt, doubly satisfied that the girls were safe in my care.

Occasionally, a visit to the field followed, but these were generally reserved until after the main event of the evening, which was Dad's return from work.

At the appropriate time, I took up my position in front of the picture window, and so accurate was my timing, that I wouldn't have long to wait before the familiar sound of our car (the Green one was a permanent fixture now, so I didn't have to learn any more engine sounds) announced Dad's arrival.

With that sound in my ears, the next priority was to get into the porch as quickly as possible. Mum shared my concern, but her reason was to protect the net curtain from certain destruction, either being beaten by my flaying tail or torn to shreds by my impatient, uncontrollable claws.

So, there I would be, one way or another, waiting in my Porch to give my "Royal Welcome".

Once the door opened Dad never stood a chance as I jumped up, one leg on each of his shoulders, my head pressed hard against his face and pinning him hard back against the door, such was the enthusiasm of my welcome. Even so, in spite of such a vigorous attack, Dad still managed to counter with some equally energetic stroking and patting.

So now I had a full house, and only at such times could I completely relax, for one missing member of the family was quite sufficient to disturb my peace of mind.

Now would follow the walk over the field, when time and weather permitted, I was allowed off the lead at the bottom of the Avenue, Dad knowing that no open gate would distract my excited bound as I winged my way, straight as an arrow toward the Compound. After my statutory wee on the first long grass I came across, Monty would often join me in a scamper until he saw me disappear through my entrance.

These evening walks were guaranteed to be the short variety, so my excursion out to the hedges and around the perimeter exercising myself steadily, was of the utmost importance.

Long or short, I was in just the frame of mind for my supper, and before I was given mine, I would curl up under Dad's "Breakfast Bar", resting my head gently on Mum's knees. The bits and pieces which often came my way were certainly more interesting than my supper, for although tasty morsels were hidden under my dog meat, such as my own personal sausage, if they were on the family menu, I had to work my way through the "animal food" before I could reach some proper, more acceptable filling.

Yes, I was fussy, I admit that, I simply *hated* most types of dog food, having to nibble it on my front teeth so as not to get a taste of the dreadful stuff on the way down. In fact I was so fussy, that I examined every piece of food thoroughly before considering whether to eat it or not, a good example being a piece of bread. I simply refused to eat it unless covered with a fair smearing of butter, often licking off the coating and leaving the bread!

Many people said I should simply eat up or go without, but my family knew only too well that I felt so strongly about my food; I would rather starve than eat something I couldn't stand!

The supper I loved was liver or mince, why shouldn't I like human food? By now I was more human than dog anyway, and if I had my way, I'd sit up to the table with the rest of the family, or sit on a comfy chair and watch the telly. In fact I was beginning to get my place back on the Settee ... couldn't understand the telly though.

Once supper was finished with, and I had satisfied myself that absolutely no scraps were left, I had to choose my moment to sneak into the front room and wipe my chops along the front of the chairs.

A thick dirty tide mark bore witness to this procedure, and naturally I came in for some correction, so I simply had to choose my cleaning runs a little more carefully. I had to keep myself clean, no matter what.

Now what gave me hours of satisfaction, was a good wholesome bone. I could spend night after night gnawing away, paws pushed tightly each side, while I lovingly licked away at the marrow inside, or scraped away at the smooth exterior oblivious to anything else going on around - as long as I was doing it on my bed.

A bone was something which improved with time, but just when it started to give off a nice mature smell, undoubtedly the best time for a bone, I would have my prized possession taken away, being left to blow down my nose as I witnessed with disbelief it being tossed out into the garden !

So when I barked to go out of an evening, I would seek it out and scratch wildly at the door, knowing full well that this action would get the door opened quicker than any other. With the door opened, I would rush in at top speed, knocking over anyone silly enough to be in the way, and gain the sanctuary of my bed to flash the whites of my eyes challenging all who ventured near.

Usually, this show of boldness would buy me a little more time with my treasured property, now smelling richly, but if Mum and Dad were really serious about removing it, then I would have no choice at all, with only a token growl indicating my disapproval. Well, I wasn't going to bite the hand that fed me, in any case, I was as soft as they come!

With the gathering up of all the toys dotted around, I knew the time was fast approaching for the girls to be put to bed, and I would see them safely tucked up in their respective rooms.

While carrying out this menial but welcome duty, I carefully noted which box was used to house each particular toy, and with this very important information tucked away, I returned to the front room. With Mum and Dad settled and the two girls asleep, the time was now ripe to creep into the darkened bedroom, and knowing exactly where to go, select the toys of my choice, padding busily to and fro, until all the soft animals recently collected so carefully, were now back all over the front room!

I would have a great time playing with those, laying on my back and holding them between my paws, prancing about and tossing them high into the air, or, if a real favourite had been selected, have a real good roll on them.

Although I never damaged any, there was always the odd flatter-than-usual Teddy Bear collected up and packed away for the second time !

So now with the evening wearing on came the time for some relaxation, a snooze in front of the fire coming in handy, but although I had a unique knack of finding a cushion for my head, this was very much a light sleep in case I missed anything.

Now was the time for the occasional game, or even the distraction of the odd noise from outside. The noise would send me charging across the picture window, barking excitedly, but sheer panic would set in if I couldn't find the join in the curtain, through which to poke my nose, at the first attempt, and quick action was required to save the lace curtain from further destruction.

The occasional game would include seeking out and fetching my ball. While I never failed to enjoy these, the games would often come to a premature end because I was simply too eager. After retrieving the ball, I'd drop it at Dad's feet, but I was so quick diving down to pick it up, that I ended up biting Dad's hand instead.

If the damage was bad, I felt most ashamed of myself and moved in to make amends by pushing my nose against his face as close as was possible without actually touching. I indulged in one of my favourite pastimes; having my nose tickled by Dad's eyelashes! I could easily stand there for ages with my nose held close enough to touch them, but not actually bend any.

Once the games were finished with, I reclaimed my position in front of the fire, waiting for signs of the mid-evening coffee.

I wasn't interested in the coffee obviously, but there was always a choc biscuit coming my way, and I made sure of not being kept waiting by drooling heavily at the mouth, getting my way without fail before the carpet was covered with a slippery liquid. Then, with the snack successfully digested, I could get on with the serious business of sleeping by retiring to my box and drifting off in an instant.

After a most refreshing sleep, a built-in alarm (the same one used for Dad's homecoming) had me wandering back into the front room to toast myself in front of the fire exactly on 10 pm, give or take a minute or two, and every night without fail. Certainly I was a classic example of a creature of habit.

Once I was nicely toasted came the time to squeeze between Mum, sitting on the floor, and the fire, taking up any shape that was left, whether it was long and thin or just a tiny square, but although part of me would drape over her at odd times, I never got moved off. Far from it, Mum pulled me further on, and as she cuddled me, tried to read my thoughts by relating them to Dad.

The fact is, her interpretation of them were not that far from the truth. Talk about dogs being able to understand every word their owners said. Mind you, I wasn't always allowed to relax even then, because if there had been a film on T.V. I was due for some more of Dad's games. The favourite was to be trussed up like a steer, while another was to have a towel waved at me and expected to charge it. He often joked about putting an elastic band around my nose and then shouting 'Burgulars', but luckily I'm glad to say he never meant it.

There, my Average Day would finally draw to a close, and as soon as the T.V. was switched off, I would make my way straight to the front door for my late night wee, while Mum and Dad prepared for bed.

After a last sniff around, I'd wait patiently at the nearest door, a polite late night yap, indicating that I was ready to come back in. If I had chosen the wrong door, a sharp rattle of the correct door handle would be enough to send me scampering round the bungalow to re-enter .

With the girls safely checked, I curled up on the sheepskin rug outside Mum's bedroom, turning round several times before settling. This sleep was only temporary, because, only once everyone was safely asleep was I prepared to seek out my box, and after several more turns, drop with a heavy crash to take my final and deepest sleep of the day.

Back in my rightful place on the settee

Chapter Twenty

My Tenth Year

Snow was enjoyed as much by me, as Katie and Lyndsey, in fact it was probably fair to suggest that I enjoyed the "White Entertainment" every bit as much as Dad.

Perhaps it was because there was an acute lack of snow here, or if a few flakes did decide to shake themselves free from their grey skies, the entertaining white carpet would all too soon turn itself into slush just as I as beginning to enjoy it. Perhaps it was that strange feeling as my paws sank into the surface, almost pleading for someone to come out to play. More likely though, it was the novelty of it all, my experience at the farm being my most interesting so far.

One day in February was to change all that, and change it in a very big way indeed.

I had already woken up to a white coating as I curtsied gently one morning, but this proved true to form and vanished long before the day was out.

Then came the weekend. It looked harmless enough to start with, Dad had just finished work for the week, and as we were now a complete unit I felt relaxed and was looking forward to the first of my weekend walks. I certainly took no notice at all of the tiny, insignificant specks blowing innocently across the garden and continued with my routine activities. I should have guessed something special was happening by the number of times Dad went to the picture window to peer out.

He was laying a carpet in the bathroom at the time, and if it wasn't for my utter dislike for that little room, I would have been in there helping, so I just poked my nose in through the door from time to time to check his rather slow progress, made all the slower of course by his constant visits to the window.

When I was let out for my final wee of the day, I began to take notice, for although the grass was not thickly covered enough to interfere with my late night duty, the strong wind was piling the snow deep against the walls of the garden and Bungalow.

I loved to stand head into the wind, allowing distant smells to swirl into my nostrils, but this time they were beginning to fill with snow, and such was the deceit of this particular wind, that the fine white particles found their way under my tail at the same time! Most unkind.

First suspicions of the spectacle waiting outside came when I was about to be let out for my morning wee. Dad had a great deal of trouble opening the front door, and after a struggle, creaked it open, allowing a huge mountain of snow to come cascading in.

I ventured out only a short distance before my paws started to sink. 'Great,' I thought, 'just like old times,' but my paws went on sinking, and sinking, until my tummy was resting on the icy surface.

I hesitated just long enough for my undercarriage to go numb, and after straining away, managed to pull myself out and, by leaping forward, managed to make rather clumsy progress.

Where were the Gates? That was the next question. I knew roughly where they *should* have been, and after some hearty digging from Dad, they were uncovered enough to squeeze through.

What an amazing sight down the avenue, through the still swirling snow, I would have been forgiven if I thought I was looking at the sand dunes on the Burrows. There were no garden walls anymore, and the wind had twisted the snow into a series of giant mountains all the way down our avenue.

Dad set off, working his way around the great mounds, but in my usual impatience, I took the direct route - what a mistake! I went straight into the first snow drift and completely disappeared! Once I had been dug out we continued undaunted, not wanting to miss any of this rewarding experience.

Snow in the Avenue

... looks just like the Dunes

The family snowed in

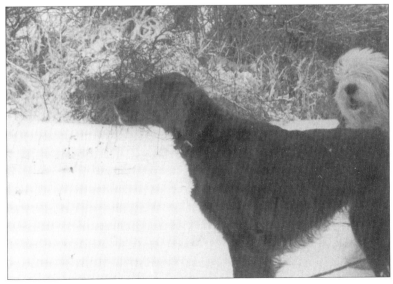

Viewing the snow with Monty

By keeping close to Dad I managed to reach the field without any further mishaps, and was then joined by Monty for some real fancy games. Jumping, rolling, prancing and skating, behaving just like a couple of puppies and I was quite sorry to return to the bungalow.

After breakfast, thoroughly thawed out, it was the time for Katie Lyndsey to join us for some more games. As we played in the Avenue, everyone safe in the knowledge that I couldn't enter any gardens even if I wanted, the gates around us gradually began to appear as the owners dug away like beavers.

No cars could get out though, and it was certainly a strange sight to see so many people working their way through the dunes and it seemed certain that this snow would be in no hurry to melt.

With everywhere brought to a complete and silent standstill, we all set off through the deep snow for a visit to the shops for some emergency provisions. Out on the main road, (at least, I think it was the main road) the eerie silence continued, for there was not a single car in sight there either.

We were certainly not the only people to venture out, because on each side of the road, a long line of figures trudged warily into the distance, pressing the snow into a narrow footpath for others to follow. I would have dearly loved to welcome each person in turn as they puffed their way past, but as each one came into reach, my lead was quickly shortened and a wag of my tail had to suffice.

The lack of traffic gave me a certain feeling of security which soon spread to some of the walkers, and a third footpath began to form down the middle of the road.

Naturally, the girls admired the fairy land covering and so our trek down to the shops turned into a most casual adventure.

With the occupants of Wynsum checked upon and some provisions left behind there, the girls set about the return trip with an equal amount of enthusiasm, only tiredness from the uphill climb persuading them to spend some time back inside the bungalow. Needless to say, we were all out again until late afternoon, with the girls making a giant snowman, and generally taking advantage of the extra helping of winter fare.

Mind you, it had its disadvantages, because the car got stuck twice in snowdrifts the following day, while Dad was trying to get to work, and we all set about digging him out and that was only in our own, private avenue

I had a great time, along with the girls, having my fill of snow - enough to last a long time. Come to think of it, Dad didn't do bad either!

With the weather back to normal, I was able to continue my walks along the beaches, but during a visit to one of the more remote ones, I was unlucky enough to damage my coat in a very unusual fashion.

The beach in question was Putsborough, little visited by us because of my travelling problem, but a fine exercise area nevertheless.

On this occasion I found a new, superb black, sticky substance called Tar to roll in. With great care and much wriggling, I found I could spread this substance liberally all over my back.

No quick bath to get it out this time, and such was the degree of my plight that I had to be "operated on" in the car park with some vigorous rubbing with an old towel, and worst of all, the contaminated areas of fur had to be cut away. What a shambles. The two girls immediately, and rather cruelly, named me a "Punk Dog".

No sooner had my coat grown back to normal, than it became damaged again, this time by the dreaded black dog.

With the girls now big enough to take me over the field by themselves, I was on my way back from such a trip with Lyndsey. On reaching the bottom of our avenue, I could now be trusted to trot up to our gate without my lead, bypass all the forbidden gardens, and make for my own, the gate of which had been left open for such a purpose.

Poor Lyndsey was just about to carry out my releasing operation, when the cowardly villain struck! Realising Dad wasn't there, he darted out to grab a lump of freshly grown fur, before running back into its garden.

With Lyndsey to look after, I didn't know what to do except accompany her back home. She was more upset than I was, and after some more repairs to my poor old coat, an old toy was dug out to cheer her up. This was an ancient Typewriter and brought memories flooding back of Mum's first job when I was a tiny pup.

Black dogs were to continue to haunt me, and one weekend, with Dad left at home to take part in a cricket match, I was taken to Saunton.

145

No sooner had I been let out of the car than a huge black Labrador called Winston came lumbering over. Everywhere that we went he went, taking a great interest in my tail end, and with my hatred of black dogs this made the walk most unpleasant.

Our usually enjoyable walk along the beach was hastily abandoned, and we returned to keep Dad company, making sure that I was kept at a healthy distance from the game in progress.

That walk at Saunton was only one of two without Dad that I can remember. The second was on a Saturday while he was working, Mum not missing the opportunity to give me an extra walk.

At first I didn't get over excited about entering the car, because with Dad absent, I thought we were simply going down to his work to give him a lift home and this certainly seemed to be the way the afternoon was turning out, when I was let out into the car park of the factory.

With Katie and Lyndsey in control of my lead, we marched smartly into the Building.

Being Saturday, obviously there were very few people about to ask directions, but Dad, in his usual way, had foreseen such problems and left large arrows for the girls to follow. Always prepared for a game, they enjoyed skipping from arrow to arrow, until, with a little help from "the Major", we found Dad tucked away in a corner of his little room.

The reason for our visit turned out to be the handing over of the front door keys, but even so, I was as pleased to find Dad as he was to see us.

After the girls had been given a quick tour of some interesting gadgets which caught their fancy, and having been seen safely out of the factory, I had the passenger seat all to myself, not to return home, but to set off in the opposite direction towards the burrows.

Once among the dunes, I felt it my responsibility to look after my companions, and make sure not to stray too far away, certainly never out of sight. Continually running in my famous figure-of-eight movement, I kept all three under constant supervision, and it was little surprise that when I arrived home, I had only just enough energy left to welcome Dad before collapsing for a well-earned sleep for the best part of the evening.

Mind you, as an extra walk, it was superb, most enjoyable, in fact, one of the best runs over the burrows since taking on the Army many years ago!

As well as prolonged confrontations with Black Dogs, the old Rover car continued to provide entertaining and calamitous incidents.

The most notable followed a trip to the Burrows after the car had been parked at Braunton on the way home. Everyone had gone in for a chat, leaving me with Rusty and Skipper for company, assuming that we would be nicely settled down on their return, and so we would have been but for the two lads' latest trick.

Restless at having been left, Rusty pawed away at the door handle, until, with a smart thump, the handle snapped down. Skipper joined in the manoeuvre now, and pressing his weight against the door, had little difficulty in opening it.

In a flash they were both out, and not wanting to be left on my own, I followed. As we started a tour of the Braunton side streets, back came memories of my main road escapade, and as the old uneasy feelings gripped me, I barked loudly, trying to warn the two boys of the approaching danger.

Whether or not my warning helped, I can't really remember, but with only one garden to pass before we reached the busy main road, the two dogs suddenly made for an open gateway and into the comparative safety of a garden.

Happily, my urgent barks had not been missed by some of the neighbours, and almost the entire household into which the family had casually strolled some time earlier, now fell over themselves in their panic to save us from the traffic, or even the neighbouring gardens from certain destruction!

If nothing else, a hard lesson was learnt from this episode, and that was, never leave a bunch of Setters alone together, because such a situation was courting certain disaster.

Events during the Summer resulted in my world shrinking somewhat, with one of my lesser-used fields being claimed to build more houses.

I still had my hole-in-the-hedge field, but the quality of walks decreased when Monty failed to escort me through the compound.

This obviously happened many times before, but when he continued to miss my walks, we heard the sad news that he had died after an illness, and I sadly missed his woolly presence after so many years.

I wasn't to realise it then, but even as I took my late summer walks, time was already running out for my personal field, and to borrow Dad's expression, "The Concrete Jungle" was poised to close in.

Now as I approached my tenth birthday, (70 dog years) even though I continued to enjoy my exercise and still covered the same distance, I was now returning home feeling quite weary and sleeping much more in the evening.

This fact didn't go unnoticed by Mum and Dad either, but at that time, we put it down to my growing number of years, even though my mental age was still that of a puppy.

I made certain to steer clear of any crowds, preferring to run quietly with my Best friends, but this act wasn't significant in itself either since that time long ago when I was taken into the park while a carnival was in progress. Such was my distress at the multitudes of people and the general hustle and bustle, that I had to be taken home quickly to less crowded pastures.

Now came the big crunch!

After the family had been to a firework display over in the compound, leaving me safely at home, I heard them talking about gate posts erected at the entrance, and how concerned they were about it. That weekend I saw them for myself, spending much time sniffing round them suspiciously before passing by on my way to the field.

What a walk that turned out to be! Fearing the gates could be strung across at any time, I was given the full treatment.

We took in every field I ever visited, mud patches included, even the cows didn't seem so hostile, and as I padded through field after field, my "feathers" and "trousers" became thoroughly caked with a most interesting mixture of mud and cow pats. Of course I was worn out, any youngster would have been after an excursion like that, arriving home in a thoroughly acceptable state, there were no scoldings, no bath, and enough smells up my nostrils to last a month!

Unfortunately, they had to last me a lot longer than that, because the following Monday, the worst fears were realised, and two large, very heavy gates were indeed hung across the entrance to the

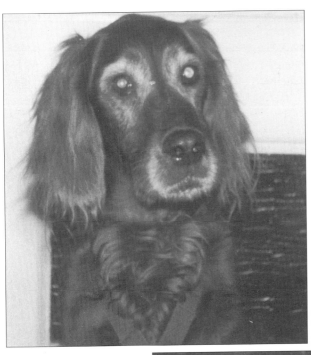

In my 10th year

compound. With that one thoughtless act, ten years of highly interesting, satisfying, and friendly exercise came to an immediate and very abrupt halt.

I missed the fields badly of course, with the nights closing in, my walks had to be restricted to weekend trips and the occasional quick run in the park, where I could come across my old friend Shamus, now demanding more respect due to his advancing years.

Once a week. I would be included in the main shopping trip, being dropped off in the park on the way home.

The combination of Dad's presence and comforting street lights, ensuring a quick semi-satisfying run in the darkness. Then of course, when we got home, there was always the shopping to inspect, I never failed to enjoy that!

Each and every item came in for close scrutiny, as I poked and prodded my way through, wagging my tail enthusiastically until I came across my tins of dog meat!

There was one dreadful time when Dad had one of him "brainstorms" as a year's supply of the awful stuff came through the door. Carton after carton was piled around my bed until I had completely disappeared, the very thought of struggling through that amount was simply appaling until a huge box of Bonios was placed on top ... now that *was* a good idea.

Something as mundane as a boring trip for the weekly shopping could provide some excitement though, and we had just left the warehouse when smoke suddenly started to billow out from behind the steering wheel. We stopped in a great hurry, and left the car rapidly. Fully expecting to bid farewell to our favourite vehicle, we soon discovered the cause of the smoke was nothing more serious than the cigarette lighter switching itself on ... I'm saying nothing!

The days were really short now, and I knew the Christmas festivities couldn't be far away, but it did cut down any weekday walks to a bare minimum.

However, there was still one place we could retreat to; a hill overlooking the town. The family referred to it as Roborough, but to me was simply a field, rolling away into the distance, and crammed full of smells and trails of the highest quality.

Being well above the town, and totally secluded, we were completely relaxed here and walks were extremely casual and relaxing affairs. Being high up had another advantage, not for me, for the girls. Kite flying.

The kite was a strange contraption, I thought. The girls would spend ages running backwards, trying hard to get the small piece of plastic to fly up in the sky. Whenever I tried to help, I simply got tangled up in the cotton, coming in for a good deal of abuse, so during this silly pastime, I made sure to keep well away and get on with the more serious business of following rabbit trails.

Then along came Christmas, and possibly due to my loss of casual exercise, the holiday produced a succession of long walks along the beaches, burrows and dunes, although on one particular visit to Instow, I thought my past was catching up with me.

Knowing full well that any beach was total sanctuary from traffic, I became particularly alarmed by a heavy rumbling noise drifting in from the Sea. In complete disbelief, I witnessed great ugly monsters emerging onto the beach, and after bounding off to a comparatively safe distance from which to bark at these sinister vehicles, observed some familiar figures marching down the beach to meet them.

Soldiers! Memories of my confrontation many years ago came drifting back, and I couldn't make up my mind whether to investigate or not, but my dilemma was short lived, as, with a click, my lead was snapped swiftly and securely onto my collar to be firmly led away. Apparently, I wasn't the only one to remember our conflict and they were certainly, taking no chances.

My seaside walks continued throughout the holiday though, and all this in spite of pulling off one of my ingenious tricks with the Christmas goodies, and completely emptying a box of Dad's favourite Rum Truffles.

My tricks were greeted with a good deal of tolerance by now, but the fact that Dad may have still been feeling guilty about putting his head through the glass lamp shade in the hall , while having a romp with me probably had something to do with it.

The presents were well up to standard, with some fine larger-than-life soft toys being uncovered while plenty of seasonal fare found its way into my bowl to cover up my normal food.

We had visits from Nana Polly over the holiday period, and Nana Grace along with Grandad George came to call on New Years Day to complete a fairly busy, but entirely enjoyable Holiday.

During the latter visit we went out on a long walk around the roads, but partly because old Chum was now very slow, and partly because the surrounding fields were full of sheep, I kept firmly on my lead for the entire trip.

I was dearly longing to bound about in the first field we came to, seeing my personal one had been closed, and as we passed one after another, my frustration built up until I was straining harder on my lead than at any time since my Puppy days.

Dad's temper was beginning to fray, and when eventually a small field became available, he proved he hadn't forgotten the knack of lifting me over a gate by deftly hauling me up by my scruff and dropping me down on the other side.

Normally I wouldn't worry about that sort of treatment, but possibly due to all that pulling, my throat was pretty sore and all I wanted to do was get home. I wandered listlessly behind Dad as he ran up and down the field, and, completely baffled by my lack of interest, his frustration now matched mine as we left the field, and I think everybody was thankful to return to the bungalow.

That walk was to prove significant, for my sore throat turned into a severe bout of tonsillitis, with me frightening the life out of the family by laying still in my bed all morning, and looking a very sorry sight indeed. During the afternoon, a bed was set in front of the fire, and I lay there forlornly until evening, soaking up the ample warmth, before struggling to my feet to receive an even warmer welcome for my recovery.

Although I felt much better the following day, my throat continued to give me trouble, and I became increasingly tired after my walks.

Such was the concern far me that I made another visit to the vet, but although the surgery was just the same, I was tended by a new, much younger man.

His manner was so gentle, that I took an instant liking to him, and while I'm sure Mum and Dad did as well, when we got home, the atmosphere became one of deep gloom. Mum was so upset that she needed a good deal of comfort from me to lift her spirits.

There must have been some very bad news indeed, because a stillness settled over the bungalow, with the girls being extra gentle in their games with me

I made a second visit to the vet, being pleased to find the same one waiting to look at me; he was actually the son of Mr. Pettett, who had looked after me as a tiny, wrinkled-nosed pup all those years ago.

The news must have been worse still this time, because the very next day, Mum took the day off work to stay at home and look after me, while at lunch time, Dad surprised the pair of us by cycling the three miles from the factory to spend his lunch break with me.

Obviously, with Dad cycling now, it didn't take much to surprise me, there being no engine noise to listen out for, but most times I would be in position in good time of an evening for the welcome, my "alarm clock" still in good working order.

It was little wonder then, as he came cycling silently up to the door, that my nervous, high pitched all-in-one barks spilled out after my relaxing morning in Mum's company. I prided myself on always being one step ahead of Dad, and always being equal to his surprises, the only other time I was caught out that I can remember was the time I poked his eyelashes only to have my nose severely pricked. He was growing a beard!

Once I had got over the surprise of his return, more unscheduled activities were to follow as a bundle of food was gathered together, and in spite of the wintry weather, we set off for a picnic and an enjoyable walk.

These midday excursions didn't end there either, and without fail on the days Mum was away at her part-time job, Dad would appear silently on his bike.

The last remaining field open to us was certainly not the best example, being completely overgrown, but with only one to choose from, it was the best I was going to get, so who was I to complain?

We did have access to an old disused railway line, which added some variety and from the far end I came across another, much smaller field to sniff around in which, in my condition suited my purpose quite adequately.

While I wandered off following the trails Dad sat on the embankment to munch away at his sandwiches. Even that simple act wasn't possible very often, because many of these quickie walks were accompanied by rain, my wet coat having the luxury of a blow from the hairdryer when we arrived back, much to my delight

Naturally, I became quite accustomed to having Dad interrupt my morning snooze, a most pleasant occurrence, I might add, and a rewarding one as well on the day he came in with the rucksack smelling of mouth-watering mince for me to enjoy after our midday excursion.

During the days when Mum was home, I had an increase in visits to the park, but equally interesting were the lunchtime trips to Dad's work.

Most times Dad joined us for a comfortable walk in the field alongside which there were many animal smells, including a very strong smell of sheep. In the far distance I could faintly make out the little woolly creatures, but I wasn't snapped onto my lead, being allowed to carry on with my wanderings. Dad knew full well that I had absolutely no intention of worrying them.

After several of these lunchtime excursions, I was taken back into the factory for another tour.

What a reception! Everybody without exception went out of their way to greet me and make a great fuss. I was overwhelmed with all the attention, but of course I could soak up plenty of praise - I wasn't too old for that!

While this was happening during the weekdays, my weekend trips consisted of a tour, come rain or shine, round all my old haunts.

We took in the Burrows, Saunton, Instow, Roborough and many, many more beaches and interesting walks. It was a really marvellous time, bringing back many happy memories. More memories were on hand when we came across some workmen laying a thick black surface on our Avenue, and while they were in no danger, with me being on my lead, we did notice that my paw marks had finally been covered over. They had remained there, year after year, through good times and bad, and it seemed sad really that they had to disappear at all.

While I still enjoyed my walks, my evening tiredness increased and I was quite happy to curl up on the settee, only stirring to go out for a wee, which also seemed to be increasing, but no one seemed irritated by my frequent trips to the front door.

The depth of my sleep was such that Dad could enter the bungalow undetected during his lunch time visits, an unthinkable, and unforgivable feat until now.

During the afternoons, I was allowed the complete freedom of the home, seeking out warm and soothing patches of sunlight to snooze in during breaks in the bad weather.

Eating was becoming a problem now, and this led to the phasing out of my normal diet, and "proper" food being substituted instead; liver, roast beef, mince and the like being most acceptable. However, even these delightful offerings were beginning to lose their taste as they became harder to digest and my intake became smaller and smaller.

My lack of interest in eating was becoming a major worry to my family to such an extent that they took turns to scoop out a handful of food, and spend ages patiently waiting for me to lick some out of their outstretched hand. The most successful at this method were the girls, but we all knew I only licked their hands clean in return for their concern.

Now even my sleep was threatened because my pencil slim body was getting thinner and as it did so, I became more bony.

Mum and Dad seemed to be one step ahead, and pillows and cushions were laid down for my comfort in an effort to counteract the effect.

Sunday 15th March 1981

As I slowed down, so my family kept pace with me until one beautiful Sunday in March when the rain finally stopped and the sun at last obliged, bathing everywhere with its bright yet gentle warmth, we set off for an afternoon at the Burrows.

When we left the car, I was hoping that the understanding of my situation would be such that the walk would not be too long, and I wasn't to be disappointed. When after a short walk we came across a cosy part of the Burrows and the family looked like settling down, I was indeed relieved and only too willing to relax in the early warm spring sunshine.

The spot was well chosen indeed, a large Dune well away from casual walkers, being completely surrounded by water and sheltered from the wind, allowing total undisturbed freedom to do my own thing. My own private corner had everything I wanted. Equal portions of grass and sand, plenty of smells to follow through the gorse, or I could simply paddle in the ponds amongst the reeds. All this beneath a vast expanse of clear blue sky.

Even when one of the family made a movement, it was only to lead me on a gentle circle of our Dune, settling down again on our return. They were only too happy to let me doze in the pleasant sunshine if that was what I wanted.

During that afternoon I made out several dogs passing. I took extra interest as I recognised the shapes of both English and Irish Setter as they scampered by, each in their own individual styles.

I was quite happy not to be noticed, satisfied that my own corner could not be shared, protected as it was by the surrounding water. On that particular afternoon I was more than content to relax in the company of those who knew and understood me so intimately. Altogether a most pleasant afternoon.

Epilogue

An era was thus drawing to a close. Life without Lola was unthinkable, indeed over Christmas 1980 there was little reason to suspect that we should contemplate otherwise.

But then, she was *only* a domestic pet after all, could we possibly justify the fact that we had allowed her to alter our way of life when the media was telling us (quite rightly) how uncontrolled animals could become a hazard to health and leisure in our society.

Well obviously the answer to that question is a resounding YES!

In spite of her natural exuberance she was always under control, her good nature never faltered, and certainly she could be labelled as only a "*domestic*" pet. Apart from hunting instincts, I'm very pleased to say her only "*working*" attribute was the deep bark, fierce enough to scare any intruders, even if there was no bite to follow!

What Lola had to offer us as a family, was comfort, companionship, (which increased as she grew older) always being around to help whenever she was needed, never suffering from our ups and downs, but sharing our life simply by being with us, as countless photographs with all, or only part, of a Setter featured in the background, will bear witness.

Any pet, no matter what size, who had fulfiled their obligations as thoroughly and faithfully as Lola would have certainly been worthy of all the love and attention bestowed on them.

The senses and instincts of a Red Setter are equal to most dogs, but the mannerisms and habits are unique, and the list of these is endless, so I make no excuses for including the following.

- Never failing to come in to comfort the girls if she heard them crying.

- Continually seeking our attention by poking us repeatedly with her long wet nose, then, having successfully achieved her intention and ruined our concentration she would hold that dripping wet nose barely half an inch from ours, until we had worked out exactly what she wanted.

- Her unmistakable "Setter Shake", starting at her head and uncoiling like a corkscrew along to the tip of her tail until every single hair had been re-aligned.

- Hated getting her feet wet on the garden lawn, balancing delicately on three paws, before rushing in to press against the fire as close to it as pain would allow.

- Yawning with complete boredom each time she entered the car, or blowing down her nose with a great *whoosh*, if a decision met with her disapproval.

- How she managed to make energetic running movements with her paws, barking and squealing ... while in a deep sleep, her barks seemingly reverberating from deep inside.

Then there were the more bizarre habits such as nibbling our finger nails with her front teeth, or licking lovingly in between my extremely smelly toes! These habits plus many, many, more, would obviously never be forgotten and her influence on our life will always leave us with many happy reflections.

Bringing up a neurotic Irish Setter, is not unlike bringing up a Child, with their artful ways and naughty pranks, indeed, anyone who had successfully lived with one, may well have found the upbringing of Children easy by comparison!

So instead of selfishly worrying how I could face opening the front door without that honest welcome, reserved for me every day for ten and a half years without a single omission, or the thought of an unacceptable quietness of a morning. I should reflect only on Lola's more humourous and typical habits which we took for granted, but which other owners could easily liken to their own animals.

Obviously I can't start without briefly covering that "Royal Welcome". With paws accurately positioned on each shoulder, soft fur pressed hard against my face, I would be pinned against the wall each evening.

Then there was the uncanny way she would make straight for her "Mum" when I whispered 'Where's Jane?'

How could I possibly forget those sleepless nights waiting for her to land with a great *crash*, after whirling round endlessly in her Box.

Her remarkable "forgetfulness" if something took her attention when going out for a wee or searching intensely for something special, thus returning without completing the task.

Being both a coward, (bark and run), and a baby, (cry at the smallest injury), her high pitched yaps when caught by surprise, would never fail to amuse.

The list of habits is endless; her ability to squeeze into any shape, no matter how long or small, curling up like a swan with her nose turned completely round and facing her tail, wagging her tail when coming across clothes with friendly smells, or wagging it so vigorously in front of the Gas fire that she extinguished it and nearly gassed us on many occasions, rubbing her head against our knees while out for a walk, as a mark of appreciation.

There were two unusual reflections; one being the time we had a touch-button television set on a trial period, which changed stations seemingly by itself, but on closer inspection, wet patches on the buttons betrayed the culprit!

Then I wondered what she really thought about me teaching her to "sing" by howling at the top of our voices and watching her lift her head to do a perfect impersonation of a werewolf! Then again, I wonder what any *person* would have thought should they have come in at that precise moment.

Obviously Lola and Setters do not maintain an exclusive copyright on unusual habits and strange occurrences. An incident that immediately springs to mind concerns a doctor's Boxer dog.

Each time someone tried to contact the doctor and the phone bell gave of a "pre-ring" click, the dog would rush across the room and push the receiver off its hook before the ringing started for real. The little blighter knew that every time the phone rang, his master would go out and leave him on his own, so his remedy, learnt from many lonely hours, was simply to stop the dreaded ringing before it began.

There are many more classic examples, continuing with my uncle's pedigree mongrel, Worcester.

Worcester was the veritable canine Artful Dodger. Living as he did in London, he had duly become a wily and knowledgable animal as he patrolled his own patch maintaining law and order while keeping an eagle eye on all ensuing events and general happenings. However, one of his more pleasurable duties was to mate with as many bitches as he could, and judging the timing of the birth of his pups with amazing accuracy, would stroll over and peer into the windows to check on the progress of Mum and offspring, not unlike any other proud father.

Veena was an Afghan Hound. Her rather sad tale differs from previous examples in that it portrays an animal's devotion to anyone prepared to extend the hand of friendship after being particularly ill-treated as a pup.

While my Sister-in-law was working at The National Canine Defence League kennels at West Down, where Veena had at last found sanctuary among caring and understanding humans, she undertook the difficult task of looking after the Afghan at home. Although understandably wary of anybody other than her own new owners, Veena at last began to make slow progress back to health and fitness. It was certainly a sorry sight that the poor animal portrayed, for not only should this be an elegant and much respected creature, but well endowed with a ceaseless store of energy. Memories of my Auntie's' Afghan, Khan, typifies this point as he found cars too easy to pursue and chased after trains instead!

Unfortunately Veena's progress came to an abrupt and untimely end one day when left completely on her own in the house, because in her own brave efforts to be with the people who treated her properly, she jumped through a closed window in order to find them.

Happily the story has a satisfactory ending, because she was rescued safely and surprisingly only slightly injured, before moved into a large house in another part of Braunton with plenty of garden.

Of course, these stories need not be restricted only to dogs, since a friend of mine explained how his cat, Biggles, had a mate who called on him most nights. He never knew the cat's name, but Biggles' pal simply poked his head through the cat flap in the door, and the pair of them would slink into the darkness for an enjoyable nights prowl!

Finally back to the Setters.

The reader will no doubt recall the story of the English Setter, Skipper, who strayed away and spent the night not in a Dog Pound, but in a Police Cell, while a couple of typical Irish Setter habits are demonstrated here by Czar, a fine example of the breed.

Czar lived in an upstairs sitting room situated above his kitchen, and finding this room most suited to his comforts, he spent a lot of his time there, peaceful: relaxing, oblivious to everything. Everything except two noises that is ...

Firstly; The sound of the keys rattling, not any key mind you, because experiments jangling other types together would not interrupt his sleep at all, but the smallest chink from the "official" car keys, and one erstwhile sleepy Setter would be lined up at the bottom door in readiness for an outing!

The second noise was the sound of a bus passing. Again, not *any* bus, but the 4.10 pm. This vehicle would have the effect of stirring the fellow out of his deep slumber and gently into action, so that by the time the 4-20 pm bus stopped outside his gate, he would be well in position to welcome the three daughters of the house, back from school.

I finish with these two excellent examples. The first portraying the "innocent wickedness" a dog is capable of, while the second shows clearly that dogs have intelligent (albeit Devious) minds capable of accessing and solving the most delicate of problems.

First, Sam, a Gordon Setter, belonging to my Mother.

No amount of chastising will detract this black and tan rogue animal from his singularly destructive path of devastation, for in addition to normal healthy "puppy chewing," he has accounted for the following:

Eight pairs of Shoes, (some savaged without trace.)

Two pairs of gloves, plus gardening gloves just as fast as they can be produced.

A Wallet. (He has a distinct liking for leather.) However he rejected the Barclay card and spat it out!

161

Countless handkerchieves.

A Belt, (leather, of course.)

Several pairs of socks. One pair, belonging to my daughter, was actually returned "undamaged" but understandably never worn again!

Add to the list a drum of goldfish food, the odd packet of sugar, unexplained missing items of Shopping, a complete Christmas Pudding mix, breaking the bowl in the process, and half a sixteen pound *raw* turkey, and you begin to comprehend the magnitude of this particular problem!

The second example is Louis, an extremely handsome Irish Setter.

We met this animal at Dulverton, and at first admired his impeccable manners, for he took the utmost care to take an extended detour around a patch of of mud before carrying out his inspection of us.

His owners explained however, that the reason for this manoeuvre was in fact quite simple, and most deliberate.

At home he was the favourite, and allowed to stay indoors ... so long as he was in a clean condition.

To this end he would hold himself for up to thirty six hours if the weather was wet rather than risk getting his paws dirty while tip-toeing out to do his duty. He knew only too well that wet or dirty paws meant relegation to the kennel and away from the comforts of the house.

If nothing else, these typical examples provide firm evidence that we are certainly not alone in our seemingly endless string of delightful experiences.

So with all her unusual habits and special moments, it was obvious that we would have more than the scratches on the doors, or the threadbare patches on the carpet to remember as the dreadful nature of Lola's illness was confirmed.

It was truly ironic that she was cared for during her final weeks by the son of the vet who had cured her unpleasant sickness in her very first weeks.

It was also ironic that in the previous November those personal fields were blocked off, depriving Lola of her regular exercise, and then in January, the famous paw marks were covered over, after bearing witness to her puppy days for over a decade.

Once we had accepted the fact that the illness was terminal and we were doomed to lose the fight, we came to the decision to repay all those years of companionship by making the following weeks as easy and comfortable as possible.

Our concern was clearly shared. On the day following the confirmation by Mr Pettett, I cycled home at lunchtime to provide Lola some comfort, only to find that Jane had the same idea and had taken the day off work to nurse her.

So sickening was the sight and speed of her deterioration from an extremely active, youthful and good looking Setter, (how could anyone not admire that noble dome, super-slim body, soft silky fur, long flowing feathers and trousers, all finished off by that fine bushy tail?) that I defied the awful cold, rainy weather to cycle home at lunchtimes, while the weekends were spent revisiting all her old haunts, come rain or shine.

In addition to the usual favourites, we took in Croyde, Baggy Point, Woolacombe, Crow Point and countless others.

During the evenings, we tried to make Lola as comfortable as possible by encouraging her to lie on cushions, while continually persevering with her feeding by offering all the favourite foods we could think of on our outstretched hand in a desperate effort to keep her strength up.

Many people may argue that we were only prolonging the agony, and they would certainly have a point, indeed, with Lola being such a friendly, faithful, and gentle member of the family for the past ten and a half delightful years, the last thing we wanted was for her to suffer unnecessarily, but being that close to the animal, we obviously wanted to put off the dreadful day for as long as possible.

We agreed therefore that when she was no longer interested in her beloved walks, than that would be the moment.

Our task was made all the more difficult because, while her physical stature decreased, her senses remained razor sharp.

During those "unhappy" weeks, she continued to indulge in her personal idiosyncrasies and in her lunchtime walks around the lower field, she would gaze through a wire-netting fence toward a nearby school, watching the shadowy figures of the children and wagging her tail at the sound of their distant voices.

So, after surpassing even the vet's most optimistic estimate, the dreaded tell-tale signs appeared.

First of all, I clumsily bumped against Lola one lunchtime, sending her rolling along the rain-soaked pavement, then, eating become almost impossible, depriving her of much needed energy, but worse than that, she ran straight into a protruding gate post because jaundice had attacked one of those beautiful eyes.

Now there was no doubt that the time had finally arrived, and after many weeks of continually rainy weather, the sun at last condescended to shine, drying out the whole countryside with its welcome warmth, allowing us to spend the quiet afternoon in that secluded corner of the burrows.

As we soaked up the sun, sheltered from the chilling winds on the Sunday afternoon of March 15th, watching Lola browse lazily through the pools and reeds taking in the sun and animal smells as only she knew how, I decided there was no way this gentle and lovable animal's life should go unrecorded, even if Katie and Lyndsey were to be the only recipients of the contents.

My determination was sealed when I overheard the owner of an Irish Setter which bounded past our Dune with typical enjoyment, make the remark of how friendly, 'that dear old Lady' looked on the other side of the pool, and realised she was talking about a dog nick-named Peter Pan by our neighbours because of her youthful appearance, only three months previous.

Monday 16th March 1981

I cycled home much the same as I had since early January, but there was no way I could hide the fact that this was to be the last time, I would take an extended lunch break in my reluctance to leave Lola and return to work. I must have finished early that afternoon as well in my efforts to get home with the family for some time in the park, before keeping the appointment I had made earlier that morning.

The sun still shone, and as this was early evening, transformed the wintry bleakness of the park with its friendly glow.

We had still not become accustomed to Lola leaving the car without the usual flood of barks, and we walked tearfully alongside as she wandered pitifully across the Sports Ground. Such was the poor animal's distress, that when she came to a pair of goal posts, she stopped and refused to go through, being unable to see both posts at the same time.

We guided her gently back to the car, sitting her alone on the front passenger seat, and still trying pathetically to postpone the inevitable moment, drove away from the park as slowly as possible.

As we travelled towards Runsum, oblivious to the queue building up behind, I watched our Setter sitting quietly beside us, wishing deeply that she could have travelled in such a manner throughout her life, and therefore been able to accompany us more frequently.

Far too soon we arrived at our destination, and having elected to go in alone, I had a long and serious conversation with Mr, Pettett to confirm that enough was enough.

As I held Lola close to me, I could take comfort from the fact that she couldn't be in more understanding or professional hands, and so fitting that a dog which had unselfishly given so much, should be treated with the understanding and compassion now set aside for her.

I had no time to convey our appreciation for the way the sad affair had been handled as I quickly left the surgery to draw heavily on comfort waiting for me in the car, although when we arrived back home to an empty bungalow, we needed all the courage available, for this was beyond doubt the saddest days of our married life.

Now with all these events safely set down on paper, perhaps I have convinced myself that I am no longer some kind of animal fanatic, and there I rest my case.

In order to keep events in perspective, I have obviously been compelled to record the final weeks in this Epilogue, and in so doing, perhaps rather selfishly shared that traumatic period with the Reader.

However, I sincerely hope that the memories gained from reading this book, will be those which our Setter has left with us: A series of continually enjoyable experiences, leaving absolutely no doubt that we shall remember Lola as an animal who added a further dimension to our lives with her unselfish and warm companionship.

It was while such thoughts were raging through my head, threatening to give me a headache I would never forget, that a commotion below attracted my attention.

Looking down at the regimented line of puppies sitting neatly along the doorway of their kennel, none daring to step out from its security, I watched totally fascinated, as the line suddenly broke ranks.

Incredibly, as I bent down for a closer look, a pretty bitch pup pushed her way through the gap, to bound forward and wrap a paw around my wrist ...

Not so much *The End*, but more of a *Paws*.

Kate and Lyndsey with our next Setter, Kimberley,
and her Mum at the Sowerhill Kennels